Mr. Oseba's Las

George W. Bell

Alpha Editions

This edition published in 2023

ISBN : 9789357958271

Design and Setting By
Alpha Editions
www.alphaedis.com
Email - info@alphaedis.com

Contents

A NOTE.

MANY regard the usual "preface" to a book as of questionable value, but custom may justify the continuance of its use.

I had long been a student of Anglo-Saxon history, but until I went to Australia in 1893, I had seen little hope for a realisation of the higher aspirations of the race.

Being an individualist, a democrat of democrats, I hold that the unit of society is its basic factor, and, while in those far-off lands, I saw a vague recognition of this truth, I also saw a mergence of democracy into socialism, that failed to satisfy my definitions.

I came to New Zealand in early 1903, on a lecture tour. I was well received; and, as I could never remain in a place over night without inquiring "who started the town," and for what purpose, I began an inquiry into the situation.

I had heard and read that this colony was "submerged with socialism," and "given over to the falsehood of extremes," so I studied the literature, I mingled with the people, I attended the parliamentary sittings, and—took notes.

I found in the Press, a broad independence; in the people, a sturdy self-reliance; and in the statesmen, a feeling that they were the chosen servants of the public, by whom a ripened sentiment was to be clothed in the forms, and vitalised with the force, of law.

I found that what the uninformed derisively-called "Socialism" consisted chiefly in a series of co-operative measures, that seemed to promise, not "nerveless socialism," but the most sturdy democracy civilization had ever produced.

In my reveries, I reviewed the old books; I re-trod the path of human progress; I re-measured the struggles and the achievements of the Anglo-Saxon race, and, comparing the environing conditions with the social forces now at work, I wrote.

Being a "stranger," I had no interest, save in seeing my long-cherished theories on the way to realisation; having no acquaintances, I had no friends to flatter or enemies to criticise; and, having no favors to ask, I found it easy, in a free off-hand way, to note my impressions with impartiality.

I clothed my subject in a garb of fiction, that I might wrest from the reader the memories of the daily struggle with stubborn facts; I adopted a style, that I believed would be appreciated for its audacious novelty, and, though the eloquent flights of my chief character may seem picturesque, he but expresses the impressions, the feelings, and, further, the opinions of—

THE AUTHOR.

SCENE I.

INCONCLUSIVE ALLUSIONS.

THIS, being a true story, with the slight deviations necessary to the preservation of a due sense of proportion, it is deemed proper to casually introduce the characters on whom we must chiefly rely for the truthfulness or otherwise, of a most romantic adventure.

In such an introduction, the Editor, or compiler—the "I" in these pages— necessarily appears, but to the Chronicler himself, who has no "poetic license," we must rely for the correctness of the recital.

Though without my aid this strange story might possibly have reached the world, the manner of its coming into my hands has made me a "curtain-shifter," as it were, in the scenes, and in this pleasing task, fidelity shall be my only guide.

I was not "journeying towards Damascus," but being weary from many wanderings, and desirous of returning to dear old London as soon as possible, at Marseilles, I booked for Amsterdam on the fine passenger steamer *Irene*—the voyage, however, to be broken for a brief stay over at Lisbon.

It was midnight when we swung from our moorings and steamed out of the harbor, and, the sea being rough and I a bad sailor, I did not venture on the upper deck until nearly lunch time the following day. I was not too well. The sea was not placid, the air was damp and chill, and—well—I was not happy.

The decks were "sparsely populated," and as I was slowly zigzagging my way along, in a sense of utter loneliness, raising my eyes, my attention was aroused by the presence of what seemed a familiar figure. It was the graceful form of a tall, well-proportioned young man. His face was pale, his head was bent forward, he leaned heavily over the starboard railing of the vessel, and I imagined that he, too, was not well. I did not recognise him, but sympathy and curiosity, and, perhaps, custom, lead me half unconsciously to his side. I said to him soothingly, "It is rather rough to-day." He raised himself a little, leaned a little further over the ship's railing, and made a convulsive movement. He was "not well," but raising himself more erectly, he turned towards me slightly, and ironically said, "Thanks, so I have been informed." The "tone" of the expression was unkind, for my motives were good and my conduct was as wise as the occasion would suggest.

His voice limped piteously, but it had something in it of old familiarity. "You?" said I. My voice also had in it to him something of old familiarity. I looked in his face. He returned my gaze. The recognition was mutual.

"Leo Bergin!" said I.

"Sir Marmaduke!" said he.

"You have come to bring unholy memories," said I.

"And you have come to reproach me," said he, in tones of agony I shall never forget.

"No," said I, "Leo Bergin, I give my hand. 'Let the dead past bury its dead.' Look not sorrowfully over the past—it comes not again—but with resolute heart and strong hand brave the future, and thou shall find a crown or a grave. List—not another word of the past; but, Leo Bergin, what of the future?"

"Thou art kind," said he, with bowed head, and in good Bible phrase, "but I ill deserve your generosity."

"List," said I again, "Leo, what of the future?"

"The future?" said he, with bowed head, downcast eye, and awfully solemn voice, "the future? Because I know the past I feign would die; because I know not the future, I am cowardly enough to live. You know, my friend, my benefactor, that I have talent, good looks, and industry, but the world," said he more sadly, "is against me."

Yes, I had heard before that Leo Bergin had "talent, good looks, and industry." In fact, Leo Bergin, on a memorable occasion, had himself confessed to me as much. Ah! my brothers, what good opinions we have of ourselves. All of us, men and women, think ourselves possessed of talent, good looks and social merits; but here our self-satisfaction ends, for the dull world, whom we could so well serve, failing to appreciate us, we are left a prey to neglect, and often to despair.

Ah! my brothers, we forget that we are not impartial judges; that the world is impartial and may be just in its conclusions. How kindly we think of ourselves! In the person who readily agrees with us, what noble qualities of soul and mind we discover. But 'tis well, for conceit, foolish as it may seem, often saves us from despair.

Yes, Leo Bergin had talent, education, good looks, and industry; but Leo Bergin, I had concluded from the occasion referred to, was erratic, "a shingle short"—in fact, not "all there."

"But, Leo," said I, "where are you bound?"

"To h———," said he, in phrase quite jocular, in tones almost bitterly sad.

"Ah!" said I, "pack your kit then and step off at old Cadiz, for that is on the border."

But the bugle blew for lunch, and the association of ideas drove Leo Bergin to his cabin, and, with a sickly promise to "come later," I was left to ponder over the strange events of life—events that often lead to such meetings; the meetings, in turn, to lead to other events, even more strange and interesting.

A FRIEND IN NEED.

Well, my reader, while Leo Bergin is below, striving to compromise with his digestion, I will relate to you some of his peculiarities, that you may be prepared for his wonderful recital.

It was January 10th, 1898, as he entered my room on Great Russell Street, just opposite the British Museum, London, that I first saw him. He knocked at my door, gently; he entered my room, quietly; he sat down familiarly, and he opened the interview, promptly. I will not say Leo Bergin, on this occasion, was not modest; I will say he did not hesitate.

Had Leo Bergin remained silent I would have known that he was out of money, out of luck, out of friends, and almost out at the knees and elbows. But he evidently doubted my powers of perception, for, with superfluous frankness and eloquent volubility, he informed me that he only wanted a "loan" for a short time until he could "get on his feet."

These stories were very common. They had been very "taking" with me, but desiring to avoid occupying a like position I had grown impatient and crusty, possibly a little hard-hearted, so I looked squarely into his fine eyes, and asked him "to get on his feet" at once.

He arose, looked me in the face, not with defiance or humiliation, not with shame or impudence, but like a man. He said, "I am down." That was evident, but the soft saying of this had always cost me heavily, and, softening again, I asked who he was and what he could do.

He said, "I am an American; I was born in Virginia, lived in California, have done newspaper work in New Zealand, and as a journalist I am in London— and down."

I weakened. The man who had been born in Virginia, lived in California, and done newspaper work in New Zealand, could not be wholly depraved, for the very air of these three favored spots would preserve some semblance of virtue.

"I surrender," said I; "express your most fervent wish and it shall be granted."

He betrayed little emotion. His countenance remained placid, but he said, "I have talent, good looks, and industry, and I want employment,—I desire to earn my living. I asked for a loan, but it was in despair, and I desired to replace my lost revolver that I might 'quit this ghastly dream called life' before another week's board was due. But under the spell of your words, 'a change came o'er the spirit of my dream,' and now I must live."

"Must!" said I, "you assert this 'must' with such emphasis, perhaps you would tell me why you *must* live? For my part I see no actual necessity for it—not the least."

A cloud was on his brow. He remained silent and immovable as a statue.

"Cheer up, old fellow," said I, "for if you desire to earn your living, I will secure a position for you."

I knew who wanted a man, "talented, good-looking and industrious." I gave Leo Bergin a suit of my clothes—just a little soiled, I confess, for, as a fact, I never could obey that divine injunction regarding the giving my brother a coat, until it was a little soiled. I gave him a strong letter to a friend on Trafalgar Square, and Leo Bergin stepped into a good position.

I was called to the Continent for a few months on important duty. Time went on and within a few weeks I received a brief note.

"Trafalgar Square,
"London.

"To my Benefactor,

"Yours of —— received. Glad,—you deserve it. I am well. I think my employer is satisfied, but I am a little restless.

"LEO."

"Talent, good looks, and ambition, but a fool," said I, "and he will never get on."

A few more weeks passed, and another note came from "Trafalgar Square, London." This was less brief than the other. It read:—

"Trafalgar Square,
"London.

"Dear Sir,

"Leo Bergin is not at his desk. He has appropriated enough of my money to enable him to take a vacation, and—he left no address. Talent, good looks, and ambition Leo Bergin has, to some degree, but he is evidently a d—— villain. What did you know about this fellow, anyway?

"D. J. FOLDER."

There seemed no vagueness in this note, but I pondered. What did I know about him? Only that he was once born in Virginia, had lived in California, and had done newspaper work in New Zealand. Musingly, I said, "Perchance the villain lied." This solved the problem for the time, for it seemed more likely that a man should even lie, than go wrong with such a record.

For the time I lost all respect for Leo Bergin. To deliberately rob a confiding employer is reprehensible, and if Leo Bergin in this had not shown himself a thief, he had betrayed an entire lack of a sense of proportion. This was one side of Leo Bergin's character.

But lapses, my brothers, do not establish total depravity, for it is reported "of old" that a gentleman, on a very serious occasion, prevaricated on a very potent fact, and when confronted, "he denied." When pressed, "he denied with an oath," and yet this gentleman has been kindly remembered and well spoken of.

TEMPESTUOUS.

The wind increased in violence. It was a wild night. The blue Mediterranean was angry, but the good ship plunged ahead like a defiant monster. For two days more, the decks were unoccupied save by the careless sailors. The tables looked "lonesome," for the storm still raged in fury.

The hours and the days, that seemed like weeks and months, wore away. We rounded Cape Vincent, when immediately the wind ceased, the sea was calm, the ship rode smoothly, the air was balmy, and the passengers, like a section of the morning of resurrection, appeared plentifully upon the broad clean decks, and were happy.

The Right Hon. R. J. Seddon, P.C., LL.D., Prime Minister, Colonial Treasurer, Minister of Defence, Minister of Education and Minister of Labour. For over eleven years the sturdy Leader of the most progressive democracy of all the ages.

Leo Bergin also appeared on deck. His smile was feeble, his grasp was languid, but he spoke earnestly of beef-steak and coffee, and I felt that he was—"better." Old Cadiz had been passed, and he had evidently concluded to try some climate other than the one previously suggested. We sat—we chatted. I was to leave the ship at Lisbon, finishing my journey by the next steamer. He?—I did not know. Strange, when we do people a favour we at once feel an interest in them. Possibly we feel somewhat responsible for such an one's conduct. Possibly, too, and more likely, we desire their success, that we may take to ourselves a little credit for a "happy career."

I had done Leo Bergin a favor, was interested in him, and asked as to his "future." His glance was friendly, his smile doubtful; he drew his chin lower on his bosom, drummed on a book with his gloved fingers, and said, "Well, I have made an acquaintance with a mysterious personage. I have talent, good looks, and ambition, but I am an outcast, and I am going on a new venture. You know the Folder episode, and, to be frank, after a serious review of the case, I question the propriety of my action, and now that the money is gone, I have many qualms of conscience."

I was not a little surprised, but I was glad to discover that he believed himself to have a little conscience, for as "conscience does make cowards of us all," I hoped for his reform.

We sat side by side, and planting his closed hand firmly on my knee by way of emphasis, he said, "Yes, I have made a new acquaintance, that of a mysterious personage, and I am now starting on the most reckless, the most risky, the most irrational, and the most romantic venture ever undertaken by mortal man, and if I succeed you shall hear from me; but if I fail, oblivion will claim Leo Bergin, and the claim will be promptly allowed. I made my new acquaintance and formed my new plans but yesterday, and I stand at the dawn of the most enchanting dream that ever lured a sensible man to ruin."

I begged him to unfold his tale, but he answered, "You are a practical man, and you would regard my undertaking as so wild and visionary as to indicate insanity, for you do not regard me as an imbecile. If I fail, only another leaf, its stem nipped by the frost, flutters to the ground to fertilise the soil. If I fail, the world, save you, knows not of my folly. If I succeed, the facts that I shall reveal will be more strange than fiction, and the results of my adventure will redound to the glory of the land I love."

"Ill as I was," he continued, "I began my notes yesterday, October 5th, 1898, off the coast of Spain, and I shall keep a true record of my doings and my observations. If I survive, which is hardly likely, I shall find you and place my notes at your disposal. If I perish—if possible you shall have them brought down to the last breath, and in every page you shall have evidence of my gratitude and my integrity."

"But tell me," said I, with impatience. Here the whistle blew, we saw all confusion, and we were entering the port of Lisbon. Time for further explanation, there was none. We separated, I to follow out well-laid plans for business and pleasure, he—well, to me it was an unsolvable riddle; but I never lost faith that, some time and in some place, Leo Bergin would again turn up.

SCENE II.

LEO BERGIN "TURNS UP."

TWO years had passed, and with all my professions of interest and regard, for a full year of that time Leo Bergin had not entered my mind, and for the whole two years, he had occupied very little of my thoughts. As a fact, save on one occasion when D. J. Folder, in forgiving jest told me that he needed a man, and asked if I could recommend a young man with "talent, good looks and ambition," for the position, I do not remember having thought of Leo Bergin.

Absence defaces memory. Ah! how quickly we are forgotten. We spend our brief time upon this showy stage, assuming that we are necessary to the world's success or pleasure, but when we drop to senseless dust, all save a few, go merrily on, and even they, in a day or a few days, dry their tears and join the happy throng again.

Later, in the autumn of 1900, I was called to Copenhagen on business, and having made the acquaintance of a prominent physician there, I was invited to visit one of the leading hospitals.

In going the rounds of the various wards, we were informed that several new patients had just entered, brought from a ship which had returned from a North Polar voyage. This would satisfy some curiosity, and soon we were among the new patients. There were a dozen in all, mostly Russians, Finns, and Danes, but at one side of the ward we noticed there were two pale-looking fellows, conversing in English.

Instinctively I walked across to their presence, when to my astonishment, gazing earnestly at me, I recognised the sad, pitiful face, of emaciated, health-broken Leo Bergin.

His eyes brightened slightly, he smiled faintly, and reached a feeble faltering hand to meet mine, in friendly greeting. There was time for smiles of waning joy, time for sighs and tears of pity, but for words, the time had well nigh sped, for Leo Bergin was close to the pearly gates.

"Sit close," said he, "sit close, for I am sailing for another port, and while I don't know the nature of the climate, there can be nothing better, and nothing worse than I have had in this world, so let the storm howl, and the ship plunge, I am not whining."

So saying, he slightly turned on his bed, and reaching a thin hand under his pillow, he drew forth a package wrapped in some soft skin, and tied about with twine.

"Here," said he faintly, "this tells the whole story. It is all good 'stuff,' but I place it at your disposal. If you think it better, you may boil it down, and if you make anything out of it, well, pay Folder, for I had a good time with his money, and now I have plenty to last me through. I don't know how, but some way I knew I should find you, and this,—it is all true, but the dreams of fiction never unfolded anything half so strange."

I longed for a few more minutes, but the form of Leo Bergin lay limp on the bed. His hands were lax, his brow wore a deathly pallor, and his lips moved slowly in inaudible whispers. I touched his hand, for I wanted one more word, and as he seemed to slightly revive, I said:

"'Tell my soul, with sorrow laden,' where have you been?"

He aroused a little, smiled, and pointing to the package, gaspingly said, "It is all there, all there, and I—well, I have been to 'Symmes' Hole,'"—and when I looked again upon that placid face, the soul of Leo Bergin had sailed for the other "Port."

ADJUSTING THE CURTAINS.

Leo Bergin, with neatness and despatch, was comfortably buried, myself being chief mourner, and "after life's fitful fever he sleeps well." I was impatient to know the contents of the package, but desiring to enjoy perfect leisure, while unravelling the mystery so intensified by Leo's earnestness, I reluctantly laid it away, to wait my arrival in London.

Time passed.

I was back at my old quarters in Great Russell Street, London. The weather was so chill, dark, and foggy, that, at four, I had lighted the gas. The fire burned lazily in the small grate. The room was not uncomfortable, but in harmony with the gloomy surroundings. I was touched by a feeling of depressing loneliness. I paced the not very expansive floor, peered through the blackness into the dimly lighted streets, paced again, lighted a cigar, sat and pondered.

Thrown back in an easy chair, dreamingly watching the graceful whirling wreaths of my consoling Havana, my thoughts on random wing soared aimlessly away, to gather up the memories of vanished days. Then, like gladsome youths on holiday, came trooping along the casual incidents of an easy life, my last visit to Venice, my run to Marseilles with Monarco's party, the stormy voyage along the coast of Spain. Ah! here, in flesh and blood with spare but athletic form, pale scholarly face, pleasing but rather melancholy smile, gentle voice and cordial, arose Leo Bergin; a thought! The form vanished, but the "package" was more substantial, and I hurriedly unpacked my trunk, and drew it forth, just as he had given it me fully three months earlier.

With a thrill of mingled pain and pleasure, I removed the rough twine, and unrolled the leather wrapping. My heart throbbed with emotion, my hand trembled, but my eager eyes beheld a large roll of manuscript neatly tied with familiar tape.

While I had not even a glimpse of the nature of these notes, I did not even guess, or attempt to guess, their character. I knew that Leo Bergin, when quite alive, had talent and ambition—the good looks for this occasion I will omit—and I knew this was a most interesting, if not an important "find."

In contemplating the situation, as I leisurely removed all surplus or superfluous covering, a small scrap of soiled and crumpled paper fell to the floor, and on picking it up, I was not a little surprised to see that it was an especial note. It was written in a feeble, but legible hand, and read as follows:—

"Nowhere,
"November, 1900.

"To whoever may find the within,—

"As I am breathing my last, and I am a little anxious to be off, I pray you to forward at once to Sir Marmaduke, Colonial Club, Whitehall, London.

"LEO BERGIN.
"Richmond Virginia, late of 'Symmes' Hole.'"

This was another side of the character of Leo Bergin. Mentally, I was in what may, I think with some propriety, be termed a state of deeply interested confusion. I unrolled and exposed to view the whole package. It was voluminous. It was composed of some twenty writing tablets, each with a large number of thin sheets, foolscap size. These tablets were consecutively numbered, the pages were closely written on one side, the first few being in a round neat hand, the skill rather weakening as the work proceeded.

The Hon. Sir Joseph Ward, K.C.M.G., Colonial Secretary, Minister of Railways, Minister of Commerce and Industries, Postmaster-General, with Telegraphs, Minister in charge of Tourist and Health Resorts, and Minister of Public Health. Rather complex, but Sir Joseph's abilities are as versatile as his duties are varied.

I was too eager for a general inspection to deliberately peruse any particular portion or feature of the whole, but there was a sufficient mass of what seemed by the painstaking methods to make a large volume.

But the mystery still deepened. Where, for what purpose, and under what circumstances, was the work done? There were here and there strange names of places, strange personages and strange events recorded. Was Leo Bergin mad? or was there, in fact, somewhere passing events that were indeed stranger to us than fiction?

My cigar went out, the fire had "followed suit," I looked at my watch with some impatience, and it showed the "wee sma' hours" had come. I was perplexed, paced the floor, and looking out into the street, I saw how the gusts of wind drove the snow and sleet along with the fury of a demon. I shuddered as I paced the floor, but how could I unravel the mystery, the mystery that perplexed me?

"Back into my chamber turning, all my soul within me burning," I said again, "Where is the key?" for Leo Bergin had talent and ambition, and while he seemed erratic, he was no visionary dreamer. While Leo Bergin lacked a sense of proportion, even in his foibles he was practical, and had at least one eye on the main chance.

"No," said I, "Leo Bergin was no dreamer," he had no fads, no superstitions, and little imagination, and he was a true Bohemian. He had a "nose for news," a genius for work, and a love for adventure that all the fiends in and out of Hades could not thwart.

But how could I unravel the mystery? Where the de'il had he been for two long years? Who was Symmes? And if Symmes had a hole, where was it?

Here I paused—an idea struck me. "I am a fool," said I—but I would rave should any one less informed regarding my weakness say so. Ah! I have it. Here it is, for he said, on our parting, as he handed it to me, "It is a record of every day's doings and events." Yes, and he said, on our parting at Lisbon, "I made my new acquaintance, and laid my plans for future action yesterday. I have begun my work, and I shall keep a truthful record of every day's doings and events, and on my return I will place it at your disposal."

"Plain enough, it is all there, and to-morrow I shall begin," said I, "to unravel this mysterious story."

SCENE III.

A STRANGE STORY.

"TO-MORROW" has come. The outside world seems glad to be alive. I—the Editor—accustomed to mental ease and physical comfort, am confronted with perplexing duties. My bills are paid, my health is good, and my mind is clear, but, confound the idea of work! I never liked work, and I fear even custom will not reconcile me to drudgery. But duty calls, and, so far, duty has never called upon me in vain.

I—the Editor, remember—am ashamed that I forgot Leo Bergin for two long years; I am more ashamed that I so nearly forgot the package, the contents of which may bring pleasure to many a curious and careworn soul, for, as a fact, I feel rebuked even by the presence of this evidence of sturdy resolve, so wanting in myself. As a fact, I know, when I care to be serious, that Leo Bergin, with his restless ambition, his tireless industry, his dauntless courage, his reckless love of adventure, and his almost insane determination to turn on a little more light, with all his faults, was worth to his kind, more than a legion of happy idlers, who, like myself, were born in wealth, and indolently dallied in the soft lap of luxury, careless alike to the sorrows and the joys of common humanity.

Well, as a compromise with my conscience—I think it must be conscience, for the sensation is new to me—I am determined to unravel the mystery of Leo Bergin's absence, and, if in the mass of labored matter, there is one thought or fact or idea worthy of his fine attainments and insane strife, the world shall find some compensation for his many errors.

With comfortable surroundings, cheerful fire, easy chair, convenient desk and table, fine cigars, ample library, a new found sense of duty, an industry aroused by remorse, and with a sense of deep responsibility I begin my work, feeling that the suggestion from the dying author to "boil it down" has vastly augmented the difficulties that confront me.

I am abundantly aware that the age is athirst for fiction, whereas I have for its patience but a plain unvarnished tale. I know the taste for graceful periods, while I can give but labored phrase, and I know the critics want only the "meat," while I must crave the indulgence of an occasional flourish.

For the present, at least, I shall "boil down" the matter contained in Leo Bergin's copious notes. In this I may do him an injustice, but I shall save myself much toil and mental worry.

Of Leo Bergin I shall speak well. He is dead—and by the world's philosophy, we should speak kindly of the dead. What a vile philosophy! Why not speak kindly of the living? Why do we taunt, and harpoon, and revile the erring soul, until it drops into senseless dust, and then, when our poisoned shafts no longer sting, feel constrained to "speak kindly of the dead!"

Oh! my brothers, be good to me while I am alive; you may encourage me, aid me, save me, and when I am dead, you have a standing invitation to my funeral, and your tongues will not grieve me.

But, goodbye, indolent reverie, goodbye dreamy speculation, goodbye ease and careless waste of precious hours, and welcome toil, for I am going to do penance, so welcome wearisome work, and welcome thou confused mass of spoiled and rumpled paper, for I long to release the winged words, held so sacredly in your perishable grasp.

'Tis a strange mystery, the power of words. Life is in them, and death. A word may send the crimson current hurrying to the cheek, hurrying with many meanings, or may turn it, cold and deadly, to the heart. And yet, a word is but a breath of passing air. This is pretty—I hope it is original, but I fear it is not—but here begins the diary, a full record of the doings and observations of Leo Bergin for two eventful years. Where is number one? Ah! here it is, a few little old crumpled sheets I had not seen. No. 1 plain enough. He began on these, and laid in his supply of paper later. I will quote *verbatim* the first few pages, as they may furnish the key to the whole.

Well, then, this is the starting of that career, I hope an interesting one. It begins:—

> "At sea, on board steamer *Irene*,
> "Off coast Spain,
> "October 5th, 1898.

"Terrible storm! The purser said we were in 'imminent danger.' Danger! how thrilling!—if a fellow were not so sick. Terrible storm! But, as compared with my tempestuous soul, the angry Mediterranean is still.

"I regret having met Sir Marmaduke. He did me a kindness; I served Folder well; Lucile, and I—a poor adventurer—became friends. *The Times* wanted me to go to Armenia; I borrowed the money from young Folder in his father's absence; young Folder, it seems, took the money from the firm's safe; he fell into disgrace with his father, accused me, and—well, Folder and Sir Marmaduke and dear Lucile, all think me a thief. Let the old Mediterranean howl, let her mountainous waves plough the ground, until all the bones of all she has slain are washed up and cast on the shores of bloody Spain, and until the Pillars of Hercules are torn from their base, and I will laugh at raving Nature's petulant moods, and go down smiling with the wreckage to death and eternal night. But confound young Folder! and, but for Lucile, I would teach him a sense of proportion. Sir Marmaduke shall sometime know that he was not mistaken in me—and Lucile—well, maybe she'd rather think me a villain, than to know her brother was one."

Well, well! "Oh, my prophetic soul!" Leo Bergin, forgive! Then, Leo was not a thief, and I, like a common fool, now that the truth is out should have known that Leo Bergin, with his fine attainments, his superb vanity, and his indifference to wealth, could not stain his hands with dishonor. Surely it was a foolish proceeding at such a juncture for Leo Bergin to die. What fine material for a romance! But we never romance. He continues:—

"This morning I discovered that I had a strange cabin mate. Physically, he is the finest type of manly beauty I ever beheld; and, mentally, he seems above our common human nature. That he is no fool is certain, that he is not insane, I am fairly well persuaded, and that he is mistaken seems hardly credible, yet as measured by all the supposed knowledge of our generation, by the demonstrations of science and the calculations of thinkers, he talks the most arrant nonsense. His splendid personality, his easy graceful manners, and his general intelligence interests one; his 'sublime gift of eloquent gab,' his seeming logic, and his insinuating ideas are charming, but the seeming boldness, not to say audacity of his statements astonishes one. But to me, he is resistless; and for good or ill, success or failure, life or death, I have cast my lot with him.

"Evening, later. Strange experience this—the storms have no terror for me. Strange! but this mysterious cabin mate has captivated me. I was so bewildered with his impossible statements and extravagant claims, and with all his absolute indifference as to our incredulity, that I sought refuge in the captain's room, and here, listening to an interesting recital, I spent four of the most thrilling hours of my life.

"The captain is certainly a gentleman of superior parts. He has a fine knowledge of astronomy, he is a master of geography, and is deeply read in the broader and more general physical sciences, and yet, in the presence of this stranger, as he seems not of our world in any sense common to our understanding, he is dumb with astonishment.

"This strange being, surely a man, for he eats and drinks and smokes, and worse, he snores, says he is Amoora Oseba, that he lives in a great city called Eurania, in a country called Cavitorus, and that his people are called Shadowas. Save that the mind wanders with an unconscious effort to locate this country, city, and people, this statement seems but commonplace.

"But where is Cavitorus? Where is the City of Eurania? and who the de'il are the Shadowas? Save that he might be regarded as a superior sample, this

Amoora Oseba—which sounds Arabian—might be taken easily for a Russian, a Dane, a Scot, or a Yankee. But whence came he? Let him tell us.

"At the captain's suggestion, I invited him to the fore-cabin, where, seated around a table, our host, the chief engineer, a merchant from Boston, a parson, my cabin mate and myself, were met for interesting inquiry.

"The instruments having been brought and the glasses filled, the captain looked in the face of Mr. Oseba, and said in manly business tones, 'We have become interested in you, Mr. Oseba, and while your statements seem most astounding to us, we have invited you to my cabin, that we might persuade you to give us some explanation of your strange theories; and as an introduction of the subject, I beg to inquire from what country you hail, and what is your destination?'

"The question seemed rational, and to most men, how easily answered! But here was a new experience. All eyes were turned on the handsome, intelligent, earnest face of my new-made friend and fellow-passenger, and he said: 'Mystery lies just beyond the visible horizon of the knowable. Because I have explored the realms of your mental and visible horizon, either of you could easily answer me such a question, and to the satisfaction of all; but as my country lies beyond both your mental and visible horizon, I can only answer by an explanation, moving or advancing such lines.'

"Here Amoora Oseba took a globe in his hand, and remarked that as educated men they regarded this as a 'counterfeit presentment' or model of the world they inhabited. He explained that for millions of years, our ancestors remained indifferent, and then disputed about the shape or form of the world they inhabited; that in comparatively recent times loving men cooked one another for believing the world to be round, and that in times really but yesterday, the most advanced people had nothing like a correct conception of the construction of the Universe.

PREMIER SEDDON AND HIS POLITICAL FAMILY.

From left—The Honorables C. H. Mills, W. C. Walker, C.M.G., R. J. Seddon, P.C. LL.D., T. Duncan, J. Carroll, Sir J. G. Ward, K.C.M.G., W. Hall-Jones, J. McGowan.

"'In old, old times,' he said, 'our ancestors believed the world to be flat. That question for thousands of years was considered settled. For a comparatively brief time the world has been considered to be round, a solid sphere. This, for this short period, has been the "settled" notion.'

"But he assured us that the propositions were equally fallacious. The whole party was inclined to laugh, but he continued. He reminded us that we all believed in the nebular theory, that our earth, with the other planets, had been thrown off by the sun's rapid rotary motion; that in rapid revolution these masses had assumed forms peculiar to their revolutionary velocity, that planets had in turn thrown off masses that had become satellites, and that form was a result of motion, mass, and volume. He reminded us of the natural tendency of matter to fly from the surface of a rapidly revolving wheel, cylinder, or globe.

"This was the case with our earth. While yet a yielding or molten mass, it whirled very rapidly on its axis, the surface cooled and became rigid, and the molten matter contracted. During this process, the plastic interior moved towards the crust, the cooling mass requiring less and less space. Thus the centre parted, and our earth became, not a solid globe, as you were taught to believe, but an oval ring, a hollow ball, revolving rapidly as do the rings of Saturn, formed under the same law, but owing to the mass in her case being greater, the gravitation of the interior held the central mass together as a planet. 'As a fact,' he said, taking a large apple in his hand, 'if the core of this apple were removed with a care that would preserve the proper curvature, I will venture to say "ovality," it would present an exact model of our world. Then the world is hollow, not solid, and it is habitable and inhabited over the oval.'

"The members of the party looked at each other with amused curiosity. 'Symmes!' said the captain; 'Hurra for old Kentuck!' said the Yankee; 'Logic!' said the engineer.

"'You smile,' said Oseba, 'but a man may smile and smile, he may even sneer, and still be wrong.'

"He looked so undisturbed, so dignified and earnest, that levity ceased, and he said 'As a rule, men accept their opinions ready made, and they only search for corroborating evidence. When Galileo proclaimed a new truth, he was silenced, by the frowns of authority. Who was right? When Bruno proclaimed a great truth, he was cooked, by authority. Who was right? All your schoolboys of to-day know.'

"'But when Symmes advanced a new theory, because the world had grown more tolerant or less earnest, he was laughed out of court, while those who imprisoned Galileo, and cooked Bruno, and ridiculed Columbus and Magellan, having grown careless, amused themselves by writing of Symmes' northern regions as "Symmes' Hole."'

"'Well, gentlemen,' said Mr. Oseba, 'I am from over the Oval, from "Symmes' Hole," and after five years of constant travel and hard study among the people of the outer world, whom we call Outeroos, I am returning to "Symmes' Hole," and this young man,' turning to me, 'is going with me to report.'

"There was no mirth, the captain drumming on the table said, 'Ahem!' The Yankee said, as he looked quizzically at me, 'Well, I guess he'll have to muffle himself up pretty good, and I think our house could give him a proper outfit,' and the engineer said to me, 'raising the curtain is the most interesting part of the performance.'

"'But this is so far outside of our experience and our observations,' said the good-natured skipper.

"'Pardon,' said the calm Oseba, 'the observations of your men of experience have but confirmed our contentions, though the evidence so far, has not disturbed the hypotheses of your theorists. But what are the observations of your men of hard experience? This leads to another line of inquiry.'

"Save by an occasional question, the silence of the listeners had been unbroken from the start. The subject had been profoundly discussed, and as the hour was growing late, it was agreed that the party meet at once after dinner on the following evening. All faces now looked serious. The captain thanked the stranger, and said, 'We met to scoff, we remained in rapt attention, we retire to meditate. To-morrow evening,' said he, 'we will question you, our worthy guest, with a different feeling. Good night.'

"What a unique experience! How I would like to have had Sir Marmaduke with us. But Sir Marmaduke thinks I am a thief and unworthy of his presence.

"Well, goodbye old day,
I'll throw me down and sleep my cares away."

By George! that is striking. The man from "Symmes' Hole." Ha! Ha! Well, I wish I had been there. But Leo Bergin does me an injustice, for I was too careless to think about his crime, or alleged crime, for, as a fact, I liked him when I met him, and in his absence, I never thought either of him or his folly.

"What fools we mortals be!" We are eternally worrying about what others think of us, when, in fact, each of all the "others" is quite engaged with his or her own affairs. What "everybody says" is usually only what some idle meddler says, the busy world having no thought or care on the matter. But Leo Bergin thought of me, well—

"I'd give the lands of Deloraine,
If Musgrove were alive again."

But,—"Never, never more."

Let us see what follows, for this is more interesting far, than a courtship. Let's see—the next day I left the ship at Lisbon, in response to mail from Hamburg. Let's see if I am forgotten as easily as he was, and what the man from Symmes' Hole had to say at the adjourned meeting. By my soul, this is rich! The notes read:—

"At sea, on board S.S. *Irene*,
"Off coast of Portugal,
"October 7th, 1898.

"'Tis midnight's holy hour, and silence now is brooding o'er a still and pulseless world.

"What an eventful day! In old Lisbon a few hours, made a few purchases—paper to hold stuff enough to startle the world—saw Sir Marmaduke on the steps of the Cathedral; he did not answer my salute. If I live, he shall know me better. If—oh, that terrible 'if'! that brief halt, that in all our hopes arises to console us, that brief halt that excuses impotency for failure, chills me.

"Had a long chat with my chief, Oseba, *re* our polar journey. Strange, I speak of this with candour, and make my plans as if it were actual, and yet my judgment scoffs at my foolish dreams, for, as a fact, it must be the delusion of a madman. So I thought at 4 p.m.—

"Later.

"Promptly at eight, the party of last evening re-assembled in the captain's cabin. All seated at the table, Amoora Oseba handed round some fine cigars, the glasses were filled, and the skipper said, 'Now, Mr. Oseba, we would like to hear further from you, for if you are insane, there seems to be method in your madness. If you are a joker, you are a most charming entertainer, but if you are sane and candid, for the world's good you should remain quiet, only when necessary to refresh yourself for further effort.'

"The captain had prepared a six-inch globe by removing the axial core, and paring down the outer openings so as to leave it oval with the outer curves for Mr. Oseba's convenience in making his illustrations—this was Oseba's 'apple,' the core removed.

"On rising, Mr. Oseba thanked the captain for his courtesy, and raising the globe, he reminded the party that he was to review the observations of experienced men in support of what to him was more than a theory. He asked his friends to fix in their minds the new form of our globe, for that was important.

"He first called attention to the fact that all the extreme North Polar regions were rich with the waste or remains of animal and vegetable life. This was 'settled.' 'All navigators agree,' he said, 'that hibernating animals, say above 80 or even 78°, go north to winter; and that driftwood comes from the north with flowers unknown to botanists. In high latitudes birds and swarms of insects come from the north in spring, and Tyson's men killed many of these migrating birds for food for his crew. In the craws of these birds there were found undigested grains of wheat, some of which were planted and grew in California. The kernel of this wheat was three times the common size, and California seasons were too short for its ripening. Now, whence came the birds, the wheat, and the insects? Plainly, from "Symmes' Hole." Greely found the ice but four feet thick at 82°, and less than two feet at 84°, so the ice would not bear the boats, and many navigators report an open polar sea, and greatly agitated waters at high latitudes.

"'By the old theory, it must be known that, at the poles, the North Star would be—must be—directly overhead, or in the zenith. But, as a fact, all polar explorers know that the pole star is in the zenith at about 80°, and that, at 83-4°, it is seen far towards the stern of the ship. If the old theory were true, this phenomenon seen at 84° would only appear after a ship had sailed past the Pole some ten or twelve degrees.

"'The fact is,' said he, 'sailing north at 84°, the verge is past, the curvature is sharper, and the ship is dipping into "Symmes' Hole." Further, at 82° north, the horizon very sensibly contracts to the north and south, and enormously lengthens east and west. This is on the verge, at the point of sharpest curvature.'

"While these arguments were not entirely new to the captain, they struck him with a new force, and the party remained silent. Assuming that he had made out his case, the Sage assured us confidently that the earth was hollow, with openings at the Poles; that the equatorial sides are about 3000 miles thick; that the surface of the interior world, like that of the outside, has mountains and plains, rivers and lakes; that it has proportionately less habitable lands, an equatorial zone of some 2000 miles being quite uninhabitable; that on either side of this there is a habitable belt of variable width; that from the sun and its reflections, and electrical phenomena, there are ample light and heat; and that about 3000 miles north of the equator, just under and opposite the Greenwich meridian, stands the City of Eurania—the most beautiful and opulent on this planet—the capital of a great and wealthy country.

"Silence reigned for a few moments, when the deeply interested Boston man, in the most inquisitive and earnest tones said, 'But, my dear Sir, as we are evidently of about the same class of goods, and were probably turned out of the same mill, how the de'il did you fellows get down there? and how the de'il did you get out?'

"This discussion, so learned, so full, so logical, so eloquent, and so earnest, should be preserved, even to the tones and expression, but I am weary, and it is late, and if—there is that 'if' again—if I live, nothing of that scene shall perish; and if I don't—and, I won't—I will have spent time enough on it, for all will probably be lost, so I will 'boil it down.'

"Well, in answer, Amoora Oseba said that it was now a well-settled theory that, probably owing to periodic oscillations of the earth, the course and character of which were not yet understood, there had been great changes in the temperature of the polar regions. The moving down and the receding of the polar ice limits, in no distant geological times in the past are abundantly evident. The temperature at the so-called Poles had materially varied, the ice-belt so oscillating that at times animal and higher vegetable life flourished at high latitudes, as is known by the abundant remains of undecayed animals still found in the ice fields.

A PRETTY TALE.

"Then he related a tradition among his people, reciting that in the far distant past—at
a time probably when the polar regions were rather temperate, and most of the human race were yet in barbarism—a small tribe of peacefully disposed people inhabited a fertile region in an open world, where the horizon stretched away alike in all directions.

Mr. T. E. Donne, Superintendent of Tourist and Health Resorts; Secretary of Department of Industry and Commerce; Secretary for New Zealand Commercial Intelligence Department of the British Board of Trade; Representative St. Louis Exposition. By his industry, ability and modest candour, and the merits of his "enterprise," Mr. Donne is becoming one of the best known Tourist Agents on the globe, and he is one of the most competent and trusted of Sir Joseph Ward's carefully selected staff.

"The chief of these amiable people was an attractive and commanding personality named Olif. This Olif had a most beautiful daughter, whose mother, while gathering flowers for her child, had been strangled by the orders of an envious and childless queen. The name of the daughter was Eurania, which means "Sunbeam." But as she grew to womanhood she so strongly resembled her father, and was so constantly at his side, that the two beings seemed a double—but a single soul—and soon the people idolised the damsel under the name of Oliffa. Olif and Oliffa, the chief and his daughter, as guardian spirits, held supreme authority.

"At a great festival, in which many kindred tribes and nations met to celebrate an historic event, a grim chieftain of a warlike tribe became enamoured of Oliffa. He demanded her as one of his wives. Oliffa declined—there was a rush to arms, and many of Olif's people were slain.

"The great King Oonah took sides with his warlike chief. Oliffa was taken by force, she was led to an altar in sight of her people, her ankles were loaded with fetters, her whole tribe were condemned to extinction, and preparations were being made for the general massacre. When the King, beholding Oliffa that she was stately, beautiful, and wise withal, said:

"'Let not Olif and his tribe be slain, but banished—banished; for 'tis not well that so goodly a people should perish from the earth. I have spoken.'

"But Olif and his followers gathered themselves together, and the warriors, joining in one defiant voice, answered:

"'While we may not hope to resist the force of your savage chieftains who would expel us, we will fight here until we all die, under the gaze of Oliffa; and,' said they in thunderous tones, 'we have spoken.'

"Oliffa, heroic in her despair, raised herself to her full height, and, lifting her hands imploringly to the National Gods, in a clear and earnest voice that made the chieftain quail, said:

"'No, my father and my people, die not, but live for Oliffa—save a remnant of the tribe of Olif. I am Oliffa—human virtue is greater than kings or death. Go to the north, dwell in the hollow of my hand, and, in the fulness of time, thou shalt return to embrace me.' She had finished.

"With bowed head and in sorrow, Olif and his followers withdrew, and slowly wended their way towards the unknown regions of the north. But a party, with the angry chief Sawara, pursued, and coming to the verge of the land, Olif and his band took refuge on what seemed to be a small island. Here they repelled their pursuers, and soon they saw the channel that separated them from the mainland widen, and they thanked their deities for their deliverance.

"But, alas! they soon discovered that they were on an ice-floe, and were moving north toward the open sea. Provisions soon gave out, they prayed to their gods, they floated and suffered, and as the weaker perished, cannibalism was resorted to—for madness possessed the despairing party. Days and weeks passed, an impenetrable fog enveloped them, and they gave themselves up to utter hopelessness.

"However, soon the atmosphere became milder, the distant breakers were heard, the fog rose like a curtain, and behold! land was near. Nearer yet they floated. Night came, the full moon shone, but it moved not up from, but along the rim of the horizon. Morning came, bright and balmy. The floe had entered a strange harbor, and soon the shores were reached. It seemed a 'goodly land' with fertile soil and genial climate.

"'But a remnant of the peaceful tribe of Olif,' he said, 'were saved—nine men, thirteen women and five children. They cut boughs and built an habitation, and they said: "This shall be our dwelling place. Our city shall be called Eurania, in honor of our lost one, and here we will tarry until we return to the goddess Oliffa."'

"'This country,' said Oseba, 'was Cavitorus. These people were the ancestors of my people, the Shadowas, and on the banks of a charming harbour they built the City of Eurania, the most beautiful to-day on this planet.'

"'Through all the ages, from barbarism to the present,' said Oseba, 'there has been a lingering tale, a faint tradition among the people as related, and a vague idea that they dwelt in a shadow, in the hollow of a hand, and that some time in after ages, or in after life, they would return to an upper world, called in nursery tales and by the superstitious, Oliffa, where the inhabitants are called Outeroos—because they dwell on the outer world.'

Leo Bergin soliloquizes:—

"What astounding folly! and yet, I am on my way over the limitless fields of ice and snow and dead men's bones, to this phantom city, Eurania. Courage! who knows, for—

'There are more things in heaven, and earth, Horatio,
Than are dreamt of in your philosophy.'"

"'Well,' said Oseba, 'these few people were of an amiable race, and a common danger, and a common sorrow, had made them brethren. Then the animals of this country were many, strong, amiable, and easily tamed; the mountains were accessible, the climate genial, and the soil so fruitful that there was nothing to suggest savagery. All nature smiled, and man progressed peacefully.'

"'The people,' he continued, 'increased, they were prosperous and happy. They had no foes—so war was unknown. The animals of the chase were tamed, and agriculture became an early occupation.'

"Traditions had been broken; back of the people there were but dead walls. Interminable ice and snow, as well as time, separated them from the past. With prosperous industry the population increased. Colonies were planted along the interior sea shores, and commerce was developed. There were no despots to despoil, no superstition to blight, no wars to devastate, no idleness to waste, and wealth, such as the Outeroos never dreamed of, followed as a result.

"The lands were held for the people, but the lands were limited, and as the centuries came and went, and went and came, the population became very dense. Civilisation and Science had come, but the population began to press upon the means of subsistence. Opulent nations arose, accumulated wealth was great, but room was becoming scarce. For a time, inventive genius helped to solve the problem, but the sorrows multiplied as the struggle was made more easy. Soon necessities suggested remedies for growing evils, which not to use meant universal destruction.

"The population crowded and the weak and deformed were 'removed.' The remedy was but tentative, and gradually the pressure grew still stronger. As the centuries passed, all the weak, the worthless, and the unfit were sterilised. The pressure still increased. The State then provided for taking charge of all the children, and only the most fit were allowed to become parents.

"Under this policy, and under wise management, the State became the 'universal mother.' Parents knew not their offspring, nor the offspring their parents, and the love of humanity and public duty became the inspiring motives of human action. Under this policy, too, have the leading nations of Cavitorus, with the Shadowas in the lead, developed their present civilisation. Under such a policy they have been able to adjust the population to the possibilities of the land, and thus while they have been building their opulent present, they have developed the finest type of people mentally, morally and physically, that ever inhabited this planet.

"Oseba explained the quickness of the soil in Cavitorus, the length of the seasons and of the days, with their peculiar irregularities. He described the movements of the sun, its appearance at various seasons of the year, and why it was never entirely dark in those regions.

"Then he recited a further tradition, relating that at the time the people reached Cavitorus, the bright star Oree was the 'Pole Star,' that it had moved gradually away, but that in about twenty thousand years it was to return to its old position. Further, that on the return of Oree—the tradition ran—the Shadowas would be released from their seeming isolation, and be reunited with their brethren of the outer world to the presence, or on the surface of, Oliffa.

"'You see,' said Oseba, 'in the development of all people their myths and their heroes are strongly allied to, if they are not the actual forces of, Nature, and all have a seasoning of truth as a basis.

"'The people had watched Oree; were waiting his return, and were alert for signs of the coming change, or, as they put it, for a "deliverer." They believed from this tradition, that they had been in Cavitorus twenty thousand years, and a confidence in their future deliverance was a deep-seated superstition, a real faith and hope.

"'Well, Oree, as seen from the spot where the first "pilgrims landed," as indicated by a peak on a distant mountain, appeared some twenty-five years ago, and, as on the very night the observations were taken a portion of a wrecked vessel was cast upon our shores, no wonder the long-deferred hope found expression in a movement for inquiry and exploration.

"'Later, a tame dog with a brass collar on his neck was taken from an ice-floe. Later still, by a few months, a small box and a snow-shoe drifted ashore. In your year 1890, the corpse of a white man, clothed in furs, was found on the beach, and the next morning two bodies of what are now known to have been Esquimaux, were found. As we lived on the ocean front, we knew whence these came. At this the State took up the work, made an appropriation, organised a party, and, well,' said he, 'they abundantly equipped an expedition, put me in charge, and I am here on my return to Cavitorus, after a five years' tour, covering the countries of all the outer globe.'"

What masterly logic! What skill in the marshalling of details!

"Well," adds Leo Bergin, soliloquizing, "if it is true, and it must be, for I am going there, how much stranger than fiction!"

The notes continue:—

"The captain inquired about the harbors along the coast of Cavitorus; the Boston man inquired if there were any gold mines; the parson, how high the Shadowas built their church spires; and the engineer, what motive power was used in their transportation.

"To these Mr. Oseba answered: 'I fear, if I should tell you one half the truth about these things we should be "discovered," to our sorrow.'

"The hour was late, and as all seemed dazed by the recital, the party dispersed, to bed,—

'To sleep: perchance to dream: ay, there's the rub.'"

BOILING IT DOWN.

Well, that is rich! Leo had to cut it short, but he saved me a lot of trouble. Let's see. Here is a lot of interesting details—interesting if life were not so short—but I'll have to "boil it down," for "spice" is the word.

The two adventurers left the *Irene* at Amsterdam, ran to Hamburg, where they remained over winter, and being joined by Oseba's fellow-adventurers, they took a small steamer sent as a supply ship for a polar party "frozen up" in the seas north of Spitzbergen. Disembarking, they joined a party for the journey further north, intending to strike the open sea at a known point. As would be expected, "the cold was intense," but the party was splendidly equipped, and progress, for polar travel, was rapid.

Mitre Peak, Milford Sound

"Oseba," say the notes, "had recourse to a magazine he had supplied for the purpose
on his outward journey. Here were supplies of condensed food, articles of raiment that bid defiance to cold, instruments which by reflection converted light into warmth, and various scientific appliances, some that practically rendered the party immune from cold, and others that aided them in meeting many dangers."

Leo Bergin had not a reputation for underestimating the trials of any adventure in which he embarked, but taking all in all, it seems from his report that, under the lead of this wizard from "Symmes' Hole," a visit to the jumping-off place at the north could be made with little inconvenience or risk to life or health.

Only once in fifty pages of notes does Leo Bergin complain of hardship. Not once does he express any regrets, and he never once loses faith in his master. Only once does he say "the hardships are severe," and then he adds, "but the genius of Oseba has made us so immune from Nature's blasts, that, on the main point, we are almost comfortable."

There were seven of the returning party, five of the nine friends, who, five years before, had crossed these frozen plains with Oseba, and the two "star" adventurers.

Considering the tales written by North Pole hunters, the incidents of this journey, from 80° over the "oval" or verge, to 60° inside, are hardly worthy of extensive comment. So I'll throw the whole journey across these trackless fields of ice and snow into the waste-paper basket, or, better still, leave them here, consigned to more certain oblivion.

Had Leo Bergin been a jester, a thousand richer tales than were ever written by those who, in search of fame, have joined the throngs that left their bones in the unknown regions of the North, could have been found in these candid notes,

"But Truth is a jewel so rich and so rare,
When found should be cherished with martyr-like care."

So I shall metaphorically skip some fifty of Leo Bergin's pages, and take up the story where the party arrived in the small but picturesque harbor, on the shores of which stands the City of Eurania, the capital of Cavitorus—just over the "oval."

Over five long years had passed, since the sage Oseba, the idol of Cavitorus, and his nine brave friends had been commissioned to explore the outer world, in search of truth, in search of laws or customs by which the Shadowas might be more wisely guided, or to find a country to which it might be possible, wise and well, to send a colony of their children. Four had perished, and these were to be fittingly mourned; but "the conquering heroes come," and they were to be fittingly welcomed, and as their approach had been heralded, thousands of richly-dressed people thronged the "water front," and the beautiful city was in gala-day attire. The description of the streets, and fountains, and parks, and statues of gold, and other eye-ravishing objects, are dwelt upon in lavish detail, but "want of space," and the love of ease, admonish me to "blue pencil" many pages of this fancy fabric.

The superb personality and the gorgeous attire of the people, amazed the practical Leo Bergin. I will here venture a quotation, then again "boil it down."

He says:—

"The appearance of the people, as they crowd without confusion along and away back the shore line, is most striking. They seem over-tall and very symmetrical in form, and they move as gracefully as trained actors. They have finely-chiselled features, deep, rather large and expressive eyes, slightly bronzed complexions, and in every curious look, gaze, or expression, there is an easy, modest dignity, such as I have never before seen, even among the rarest few. In every face there is a deep and real joy; but of enthusiasm, emotionalism, or sensationalism, there is really none. This passion of the animal has gone, and the pleasures of the intellect have re-moulded the countenance. The face has become the mirror of an exalted soul. On no countenance is there seen gravity, on none hilarity.

"Seeing no sadness, I said, 'Where are the friends of the four who perished?'

"Alas! under their system none can know father or mother, sister or brother, son or daughter. All are children of the State. In the success of any one, there can be but a common joy; in failure, but a common sorrow."

What nonsense, to talk of such a society! People who forget their own children? But Herbert Spencer tells us of a people among whom the men had more affection for the children of their sisters than for those of their own wives! Mayhap, Herbert was wrong, for this seems unnatural. Mayhap, Herbert was right, for what we call "natural" is really but custom. However, "maybe" there were "reasons" in that case—experience.

Leo continues:—

"The attire, too, of these people was 'gorgeous beyond description.' Array all the royalties, all the nobility, all the Popes and the Cardinals, with all the courtly favorites and all the Rajahs and robber chieftains of all the Indies, and all the flunkies, the fops and the fools of all the capitals, great and small, of the pretentious upper world, and marshal them for comparison in ranks facing these, and they of the upper world would seem but a pitiable show, or at best an amusing burlesque.

"Silks and splendid fabrics, not loud and gay, but rich and rare; jewels resplendent with Nature's lustre, but worn as modestly as to seem but articles of common use, were present in enormous profusion. For jewels, for articles of personal adornment, for ornaments or trimmings of wearing apparel, gold was too common, cheap and vulgar. In carriages, in furniture, in statuary, in architectural adornments, it was in use by the ton—yes, by the cord. Ye gods, if the Americans knew this!

"Here, as superstition has not blighted, monopoly has not diverted, despotism has not robbed, war has not wasted, vice has not withered, wealth has grown with the ages.

"As our whole party were attired in very modest European dress, we must have appeared rather uncouth to the people, but the absence of apparent curiosity or inquisitiveness, was surprising."

The notes continue:—

"These people must be adepts in electrical science, for the air was full of 'floaters,' or flying machines, each seating one or more persons. They were as thick as blackbirds in a Missouri cornfield."

He noticed an entire absence of children from the throngs of people, but soon an open space was formed by the crowd falling back, when several thousand "youngsters" of both sexes, and all the tender ages, came marching down the wharf, in charge of a few modest-looking superintendents. As they came to a halt, the people raised their hats in salutation, when the children, seemingly all of one accord, bent a knee in acknowledgment.

The notes, observations, and running comments of the observing Leo are worthy of full perusal, and indeed of preservation, but as I am hurrying on to a definite purpose, brevity seems to be a necessity.

The reception of the party by the City Council and a joint committee from the great college, of which Leo learned that Amoora Oseba was the head, was most impressive, and when the master of ceremonies waved his hand as a signal, there was an unanimous shout of "Welcome home, Oseba! Welcome back to Eurania!"

This was the only noisy demonstration. "Every face," says the chronicler, "looked respectful, grateful, gratified, and happy, but there were no fire-crackers or bad breath."

Is not that marvellous? Think of such a people! Think of an occasion of like character in London, New York—ah, ye gods!—in Paris or Berlin! I wonder if this fellow was not spreading it on rather thick?

But, listen:—

"We were escorted to our carriages, one hundred gorgeous electro-motors, literally made of gold and ivory, and adorned with what appeared to be precious stones, but what proved to be common, indeed. We were driven to the temple—and such a temple! The Palace of Westminster, the Vatican, or the Washington Capitol would be 'nowhere.'"

But I must "boil it down." He tells us that the ceremony at the temple was "splendid, but brief"; that the reception of Amoora Oseba was sincere, and that the proceedings of the meeting of over five years previous, commissioning him for the perilous journey, were read.

"Resolutions of regret" for the loss of members of the party were passed, and a meeting was appointed at which Amoora Oseba should make his report to a select committee, and through such committee to the people of Eurania and Cavitorus.

Speaking in much praise of the almost depressing dignity of the ceremony, the notes record that at the close of the announcement, the chairman read the commission under which Oseba had acted, and on the performance of which authorised duty he was to report. It read as follows:—

"City of Eurania, Cavitorus,
"Year 20993, P.C.

"To the well-beloved Amoora Oseba, Chief, National Academy of Science.

"We, the representatives of the State, on behalf of all the Shadowas, believing that the time is approaching when, according to our traditions, we are to be reunited with our brethren of the outer world, and recognising the necessity of discovering a broader field for the expansion of our race, hereby authorise you to proceed to the discovery of any country, to study the condition of any people on this or any other world, to learn lessons of wisdom whereby we may be better governed, or 'spy out' a land to which, if possible, we may desire to send a colony of our surplus population, and to report at your discretion. The time, the necessary means, the associates, and all other matters pertaining to this unique enterprise, will be granted by the State at your discretion, and may the gods favor your undertaking, and send you back to us with improved health, increased knowledge, and hopes that may guide the Shadowas in their future struggles for social progress.

"Signed by a hundred of the National Committee."

My word! pretty good billet had this Amoora Oseba. No wonder Leo Bergin was captivated by the fellow. But that journey over the "oval," as he calls it—excuse me—it makes me shiver.

Well, according to the notes, it's a week before that meeting takes place, a week to be thrown away, to wait. Queer, it seems almost as though I was there. Let's see if there is anything in his notes to bridge the time.

Mount Cook, Mueller Valley.

Yes, here he relates what a thrilling adventure he had in a "soar" over the fifty-story houses in an electric air motor; that the buildings are made of indestructible material; how their steel does not rust; how light their machinery; how beautiful the girls. Ah, yes! And then he says: "It might be nice not to have to 'ask papa,' for here no girl has a father, a big brother, or a pretty sister—which may be convenient." But from the luxury of a mother-in-law, the Shadowas are forever cut off.

"The freedom of association between the sexes," he says, "is surprising, but the social dignity and decorum are even more surprising. The country, with every inch cultivated, is beautiful, and the aspect of Nature, especially in the night, with the moon sweeping along the opposite rim of the earth, the sweeping of the sun along the horizon, the reflection of light from unknown sources, the wonderful play of electric phenomena, are too awe-inspiring for description.

"Gold is more plentiful than iron is with us, and platinum more plentiful than silver;" and he accounts for the great quantity of these heavy metals on scientific theories. "As for diamonds and other precious stones, it is only a matter of 'grinding;' but the 'brilliants' are more beautiful than with us, owing to the peculiarities of the light."

What fairy tales! And yet we don't "know." Nature tells some strange stories. Yes, and so do people. There is something amusing or interesting in the notes of every day, but let the week slide, for we want to hear the report—we want to hear what Amoora Oseba thinks of the people of the "upper crust."

"Oh! wad some power the giftie gie us,
To see oursels as ithers see us,
It wad frae monie a blunder free us."

Possibly.

Here we come to that great meeting. Let's get down to date again, and Leo Bergin's notes.

He says:—

"Eurania, Cavitorus,
"October 5th.

"'To-morrow,' yes.

"'To-morrow, and to-morrow, and to-morrow,
Creeps in this petty pace from day to day,
To the last syllable of recorded time,
And all our yesterdays have lighted fools
The way to dusty death."

"To-morrow! the great event opens. How like a dream it all seems. But,

"Dreams in their development have breath,
And tears and tortures, and the touch of joy.
They leave a weight upon our waking thoughts,
They take a weight from off our waking toils.
... They speak,
Like symbols of the future.'

"Ah, this dreamy reverie! It brings back the vanished years, for

"'Twas just one year ago to-day,
That I remember well,'

when I began this record, at sea, on board the S.S. *Irene*. I wonder if Sir Marmaduke ever thinks of me. If he does, he thinks me—well, it doesn't much matter now. He was a good sort, however, and I will never forget him."

Kind of you, Leo Bergin. By golly! that fellow has a heart, and a head, too, for that matter, for he is rarely far wrong. He continues:—

"Yes, he was a generous old soul. Rich, good-natured and careless, but just. He read everything, but—well, perhaps if I had read as much as he, I would have thought and known as little."

Leo Bergin, I swear I had rather you had forgotten me. That's a nice way to speak of an absent friend. There is evidently a coolness between us. Yes, a cool belt, so I will keep my temper.

Proceed, Leo:—

"Had a note from Venesta to-day, and I don't know whether it gives me more pleasure or sadness. Think of courting a girl, who never had a father or a mother, a sister or a brother! Daughter of the State! Marry the daughter of the State! Ye gods, what a mother-in-law!

"I have idled away the day, and how can I make amends, save by confession and the forming of new resolutions? Well,

"'I resolve! yes, I resolve!
And then I sit me down
And watch that resolution die.
But, "To-morrow"—'

"Eurania, Cavitorus,
"October 6th.

"How balmy the air! How grandly the old sun sweeps along the rim of this great world! For one such scene New York would give a 'million,' and every eye would dim with watching the face of the flaming wheel, and every neck would ache, and every soul would shudder with awe. But, would not the Shadowas like to see Old Sol passing over their heads every twenty-four hours, and give them three-hundred and sixty-five days during the year, instead of having him whirl about their heads, hip high, giving one night seven months long, and but a hundred and sixty days of variable length? But it's all in being used to things.

"Well, I must off to the meeting. I am invited to the platform, and I shall have plenty to record this evening, for to-day is nineteen hours long. Oh, how weird!

"Later, evening.

"What o'clock is it? I don't know. I know it was nineteen hours after the old sun first flitted around Mt. Lena, that it finally retired, and how can a 'new chum' keep track of his running on such erratic lines? To make it more confusing, this is the self same old sun that mine eyes have been looking upon for, lo! these thirty wasted years. Who would have thought that sedate old watchman could ever play such pranks? Then, too, on the same little old world! Am I waking? Am I sane, or is this but a hideous delirium?

"I feel sure that all is unreal, that I am the sport of some jesting destiny—but I will play my part; then, if the vision be not a mockery, I will not have wasted too much time.

"What an eventful day! Yet, as long as it has been, or even seems to have been, every hour has been crowded with bewildering incidents—only bewildering to me, however, for how unlike the hurry, the confusion, the bustle, the noise and hilarity seen on such occasions on the upper crust! How different from a horse-race in England, an election-day in France, or a Fourth of July in America!

"What a happy, orderly, handsome, and amiable people, these. Even their Deities are amiable. Their temples of worship breathe, not only hope for the future, but appreciation for the blessings of to-day. With them, it is not a crown of glory afterwhile, but a living joy. Without the sorrow of Gautama, the gods of this under-world are as loving and as amiable. But why should not the Deities be amiable?

"'God made man,' the preacher saith,
'From a handful of dust, by a whiff of breath.'
'No,' say the sages, 'man made God,
From nothing at all, by creative nod;
Organ for organ, and limb for limb,
In the image of man, created he Him.

"These people evidently made their Gods, for they admit it. I wonder if we made ours?"

Careful Leo!

"What a wonderful city is Eurania! What a wonderful country is Cavitorus! What a wonderful people are the Shadowas!

"But that meeting! The calm dignity of those four hundred Councillors of State was amazing. What marvellous dispassionate interest is taken by the enormous throngs of people, who occupy the main body and galleries of the Temple.

"Proud Oseba! Well may I call thee 'master.' Oh! how I wish the appreciative Sir Marmaduke were here."

Yes, Leo, I would like to have been with you, but, maybe, that would have meant that I would be with you now, out of the cold, poor fellow!

But here the fellow strings it out as though our days were also nineteen hours long, and our lives a thousand years. He keeps us on so high a key, that we begin to wonder what there is in it for him. I will "blue pencil." For the once impatient Leo Bergin has forgotten, I fear, the customs of this upper world, and that every ear is attuned to the popular rush.

If you've something good to say,
Get a move!
If you'd have us go your way,
Get a move!
If it's goods, fling out your sample,
If religion, show it's ample,
But—Get a move.

'Pon my word! Leo's "borrowed lines" inspire me with a poetic vein. But Leo is becoming as tedious as an Australian drought, a West Coast "wet spell," or a debate on a "no-confidence motion," so I shall here draw my critical pencil through many lines. Leo Bergin is clearness itself, and from his language there flows, to the intelligent brain, a true conception of the situation; but for the sake of brevity—from vanity, maybe—I shall condense, in my own language.

Well, at the appointed time and place the people assembled. The four-hundred members of the Council of State occupied favoured seats in front of the platform, while many thousands of the citizens filled the stalls and ample galleries. It was an impressive scene. The meeting once called to order, "Music, such as heard outside of Eurania or heaven was never, burst upon the ear."

That's Leo's, but I shall be more prosy and more brief.

When the last strains of music had died away, and the applause ceased, the chairman arose, and after giving a brief but comprehensive review of the national traditions, the discoveries and events that led to these unparalleled adventures, he re-read the commission under which Amoora Oseba acted, and impressed upon the audience the importance of the report from the lips of Eurania's most gifted son, and the world's most intrepid explorer.

The chairman said, in opening the proceedings, that while little real attention had been given to the vague traditions that had floated down the centuries, there had always been a feeling among the Shadowas that they were in a most peculiar situation, and that science would some time solve the mystery that seemed to hang over them.

He said, since the dawn of civilisation there was an "absolute knowledge" that they were on the inner surface of a hollow planet, and there was a vague belief that there were like beings on the outer surface.

He explained that, through the enterprise of the Council of State, and the intrepidity of Amoora Oseba and his brave comrades, that question, the most momentous in the long history of Cavitorus, it was hoped, had been solved, and they had met to hear a report on that most interesting matter.

He said, as the Committee had given the most careful attention to the books, maps, charts, and globes brought by the returned party, and having had the generous assistance of Oseba himself, and Leo Bergin, a native of the upper world, they had familiarized themselves somewhat with the geography, history, customs and manners of the various nations of the upper world, by the assistance of the views to be presented, a fair understanding would be easily reached. Then, too, as the press had been generous and enterprising, he thought the people were quite prepared for an intelligent appreciation of the gifted traveller's oration. "Mr. Oseba, the father of the new philosophy," said he, "will now speak to us, as to his children."

However, as the people had requested that the poetess Vauline be permitted to ask for occasional explanations, this was provided for.

Here the record tells us—I have boiled out twenty pages of delightful "toffy"—that the chairman introduced Amoora Oseba as: "The most intrepid explorer the world ever knew," at the same time inviting Leo Bergin and the other members of the returned party to the platform.

Of this episode of the ceremony, the modest Leo Bergin says: "I was embarrassed."

A fine canvas, some sixty feet square, had previously been raised at the end of the hall, and, with the assistance of attendants, a large instrument, from which could be thrown moveable views of the earth's surface, was properly adjusted. With an explanation all too brief, as Leo himself thinks, the first picture was thrown on the wall. It was our planet, represented by a globe forty feet in diameter, revolving slowly on its axis. It was a true model of our globe, on Symmes' theory, the angle to the axis being 23°, with the north opening plainly visible, and Cavitorus was easily located.

This, we are told, was entirely novel, even to the Committee; but so skilful are the mechanics of Eurania, that from a small model or instrument taken across by the party, this wonderful piece of complicated mechanism was perfected.

What a revelation this must have been, bursting so unexpectedly upon the astonished gaze of these strange people!

But as in the magic hand of the "loved and lost" Leo Bergin there are both pen and brush, I here invoke his genius, for my pen falters.

He says:—

"As the vast assembly gazed in almost breathless awe, the master said: 'This is Oliffa, our own planet, as it is hurled through space at 68,000 miles an hour, with this brief forty feet expanded to 8,000 miles.'

The Drop Scene, Wanganui River.

"I looked into the faces of the most intellectual, the least emotional, and most observing people I have ever seen, and yet no pen, no brush, no imagination could reproduce that scene. Considering the intelligence and the unemotional character of this vast audience, the evidence of surprise was really alarming. For once, these people acted almost like we fools of the 'upper crust.'"

Humph! it makes me crawl.

"The sitting was adjourned."

I'm glad of it, for it makes me shiver. But it seems to me, considering the cool intellectuality of the Shadowas, that Leo Bergin is drawing that rather long. Let's see! These Shadowas are a very intellectual, a very thoughtful, a very cultivated and civilised people. But let us reason this out. They were utilitarian; amiable as their environment, and learned, in what was necessary for their happiness, or within their reach. Yes, but nine-tenths of the universe—of the outer world—was shut off from them. They, for 21,000 years, had been on one side—the inside—of a great tube. Practically back of them, the world lifted abruptly up; front of them, they could but see above the rim of the bowl of which they were well toward the bottom.

The field of observation was narrow, the visible facts of Nature were few. At the near opening of the "tube" there was eternal ice and snow, an endless expanse of frozen mystery; while at the other, there could sometimes be seen many weird clusters of stars, but, usually, only clouds and storms, and desert and mountains, and dangerous whirlpools.

They had no telescopes; their point of view was too narrow for the study of astronomy, and, as all thoughts, all ideas, all conceptions of all natural objects must be formed from observation—from sensuous impressions—how could they draw anything like correct conclusions regarding the outside worlds? Intellectuality does not always, if ever, mean universal, or even very great, knowledge.

Well, then, maybe Leo was even drawing it mildly. Maybe, a vision so strange, a view of a known thing from so surprisingly unexpected a standpoint, at a time, too, when the public imagination was at a high tension, presenting so strange a phenomenon, would affect the fine but impressive mind more than it would the less thoughtful. Maybe, I say, Leo is right, but it seems a little lofty.

But let's back to Leo's notes. He says:—

"After lunch"—that sounds familiar—"the meeting recommenced, and the people, having conversed fully and freely over the matter, seemed in their normal condition.

"Oseba turned the globe slowly, explained the nature of the earth and of the sun, why the days were 'thusly'; then the 'outside' conditions, and why it was not all eternal frost, as they had imagined. He showed the map of land and water, how there were on the outside of our planet, or Oliffa, 1,400,000,000 of people—a few of them very decent fellows—and suggested the enormous importance of communicating with them.

"Then he showed a globe, with continents, islands, seas, rivers, and the geographical divisions of the land as claimed by nations, empires, states, and communities, making suitable remarks, that his impressions might lack nothing in clearness.

"He explained that the varied blocks and patches, distinguished by colored lines, marked the 'possessions' and claims of various races, nations, or political communities. He here described the enormous waste of water, and mountains, and uninhabitable land, and how little really desirable country there was on the outer surface of Oliffa. Yet, he told his audience that the Outeroos did not dwell in peace together, but divided the land according to might, and lived isolated in semi-hostile communities. 'These,' said he, 'are the lands, the countries, and the peoples I have "discovered."'

"But, he said, while the nature and necessity, the hopes, the aspirations, and the desires of all men were much the same, there existed on the outer surface of Oliffa such a variety in customs and manners adopted for the accomplishment of desired ends, that only by a visit to, and a study of, all countries, could the object of his mission be fulfilled, so for five years he and his companions had wandered, observed, and taken notes, and now it was only by reviewing the situation with some detail that an intelligent understanding could be conveyed.

"Here he pointed out on the maps the localities of the various countries, briefly describing the climate, soil, and style of government in general, and said he would now discuss a little more fully the merits of the various countries and peoples—with his conclusions from the inquiry—for his discoveries had been important and many.

"He reminded his audience of the prime purpose. His mission was to gain from the outer world a knowledge that might aid them in the better management of their domestic affairs; to discover, if possible, a country to which they might send a colony of the surplus population, and to find a people with whom they could open communications, that they might become co-workers to the mutual happiness of the newer and the older inhabitants of the world.

"Oseba," says the record, "re-arranged his instruments, saying that he would show us, as occasion required, the globe as a whole or a sectional map. He would begin his review with a country, probably the oldest settled, and certainly the most populous, on the outer surface of Oliffa—that of the Chinese Empire."

Here, I may remark that I have carefully studied the notes of poor Leo Bergin. They are full, carefully revised, and show a masterly understanding of the situation, but they are too copious for even extensive quotation. From many closely and well-written pages, the notes report Oseba's orations, with hardly a break or comment. For the sake of brevity, I shall appropriate Oseba's story, and, save by a few pointed quotations, I shall use my own language in the review of the next scene. I realise that by this method the story will be marred, the language will be less picturesque and expressive, and probably less correct, but it will be economy of space, and, what is of importance to me, "economy" in the expenditure of intellectual force. That is worthy of consideration!

The imaginative Leo seemed to be absorbed in the changing scenes of the unique situation. During a lull in the proceedings he notes:—

"How like a dream! Oh, my soul, how I do hope!"

But, probably being again confronted by that "if," he seems to hang his head, halt, and ponder, for he writes:—

"Hopes, like joys and promising children, grow into regrets, or wither and die."

SCENE IV.

FIRST "DISCOVERY."

SIZING UP AH SIN, AND LU.

THE sage Oseba, after locating China on the globe, threw a view of the map of the Empire on the wall. He explained that this country "embraced" 4,000,000 square miles of the surface of Oliffa, and contained about 400,000,000 "souls," or nearly one-third of all the Outeroos. But this includes the Mandarins, who are not supposed to have "souls."

With amusing speech, he reviewed the history, the social, political, and industrial conditions of this "peculiar" people.

It was in China that Oseba became first acquainted with the aggressiveness, the pretentiousness, and the real power of the European or Occidental Nations. As a race, these "foreign devils" were taller in stature, stronger of limb, and lighter in complexion, and they had better opinions of themselves than the Orientals. Conceit is a strong factor in all these mighty games.

The clergymen, or missionaries, were among his first acquaintances from over the seas.

A mischievous consular clerk, he says, who seemed to have a grievance, used to sing:—

"They came in shoals,
To save the souls,
Of Hop, Lee, Sing, and Wu.
They gathered gear,
Both far and near,
As you or I would do."

These "solemn men," as Oseba called them, apologising for the digression, came first of their countrymen, not for "filthy lucre," but to "save all the sons of Confucius and to take them to Heaven, where, together, they could sing and associate forever, and forever, and forever." "This," said Oseba, "seemed kind of them," but he soon learned that the nations who sent these agents to prepare the social situation for "the sweet by-and-bye," were "not at home," to Hop, Lee, Sing, or Wu, during their brief stay on the surface of Oliffa.

"We love you," said the genteel agents of a hundred disputing creeds, "go with us to a land that is better than day."

"Velly well," says Hop, Lee, Sing, and Wu, "we likely go 'Melica."

"Nay, nay!" says the good shepherd, "afterwhile, in the sweet by-and-bye. 'Tis of a better world we speak—patience, meekness, and love."

"Why," asked the poetess Vauline, "are the other Outeroos not 'at home' to the Chinese while they are quite alive?"

With a smile, Oseba said, "The Chinese, my children, are very industrious and frugal."

"Are they an inferior race?" asked the poetess Vauline.

"They are 'different,'" said Oseba, "but every race, people, nation, tribe, or creed on Oliffa, thinks itself 'superior' to any and all others. Vanity is absent—with few of the Outeroos."

At considerable length, he reviewed the political, social, and industrial situation of China, and said:—

"All the outer world might learn lessons of patient industry from China, but for us, there is nothing in China."

After a brief review of the social and political situation of each, he dismissed all the countries of Continental Asia, but he said Hongkong and Singapore, two of the world's modern wonders, had done much to apprise the world of the hidden treasures in these Tartarean regions.

He drew attention to his discovery of Japan, as it appeared on the map with Asia, and then removing this, he threw the globe on the canvas. He dwelt in almost raptures on the beauty of the country he was now to examine. Of the Japanese, of whose condition he would first inquire, he said they had an old history. They had been isolated for many centuries. They dreamed in their narrow world, played in their little backyards, worshipped their monarch, and had been happy; but recently, touched by the magic wand of modern civilisation, they aroused, and having for a brief spell cast about them, they "girded up their loins"—tightened their belts—and hurried to join the front ranks of the army of progress, with an enthusiasm, and even a wisdom, never before known on this little globe.

Cathedral Peaks, Lake Manapouri

Once aroused by the exhilarating thrill of progress, they as readily adjusted themselves to the peculiar conditions of their natural environments as children to a new playground. The mountains suggest liberty, the seas adventure, and to the fearless adventurers of those inhabiting the indented shores of the water-front, are the Outeroos indebted for all the blessings of modern progress—for civilisation is the ripened fruit of ocean commerce.

"But," said the sage Oseba, "the present 42,000,000 Japs have but 147,000 square miles of dirt, half of which is waste. Under the delirium of modern conditions the population is rapidly increasing, and thus are the inhabitants already beginning to crowd each other. The nation is becoming wealthy, while the people are becoming poor. The real estate on little Oliffa is already staked out, and conspicuously adorned with that strange device—'keep off the grass.' There is no vacant corner for the surplus population, my children, and the Japs are land animals."

The sage Oseba told his audience that "Many nations among the Outeroos regarded the 'Japs' as an 'inferior race,' but if the achievements of man is the measure of the soul and the intellect, the Japs have no superiors on little Oliffa, for her recent progress pales the lustre of the world's authentic history; but,

'If the zenith of strife, sheds a mystical lore,
And coming events cast their shadows before,'"

said the sage, as he tortured the immortal Thomas, the brilliancy of Japanese story may soon wane, and as, owing to lack of room, her only path to glory is through unfashionable war, the prospects are not rosy. Though that nation may, for a long time, remain flamboyant, the people may soon writhe in a lower misery than 'pagan Japan' ever knew.

However, should the little brown man clip the claws from the Russian bear, and send him back, lame and growling, to his northern lair, and then arouse China, and, by the skill of his wonderful capacity, organize it, Eastern Asia may remember a few thousands of the "insults" heaped upon her people during the last half-century, and conclude to test the question of "superiority" by other than industrial methods.

Of the known Monarchies of Asia, he said, the people were ignorant and impoverished, the officials were insolent and corrupt, the rulers were vicious and despotic, and the governments rotten beyond cure.

As to India, the sage Oseba spoke with sympathy. "Britain," he said, "is the only country capable of governing an 'inferior' race. She has done much to rescue the country from periodic, if not from almost constant war, and famine, and despair; but the 'people,' the offspring of thousands of years of misrule and oppression, have reached a condition of crystallized non-progressiveness, and they must finally die out, as they cannot adjust themselves to modern conditions. Its past is sad, its future is hopeless. It will long be a country in which a few cunning bees may load themselves with golden honey, that their far away hives may be filled; but slowly and sadly that strange brown people must pass away. They have reached their ultimate. In them the oak and the steel, necessary for the contests of the future, are wanting."

EUROPE, SOMEWHAT "DISCOVERED."

The globe was so adjusted as to give a perfect view of the Continent of Europe, and, in interesting speech, were the countries and their peoples described.

Referring to the influence of environment, the orator explained how the comparative smallness of this continent, the fertility of the soil, the variety of plant and animal life, the mountains, and plains, and indented shore lines, with enormous stretch of water-front, together with its extensive river systems and healthful, but erratic climatic conditions, marked this as the garden and nursery for the most active, sturdy, intelligent, and emotional of all peoples on the globe.

Continental Europe covers an area of 3,500,000 square miles, and supports, in various degrees of opulence and wretchedness, some 380,000,000 people—chiefly men, women, and clergymen—with 20,000,000 men in "uniform," who seem well seized with their own importance. These latter are very influential personages, as they are equipped with very persuasive arguments.

The orator explained that the many-hued and irregular patches on the map represented the possessions and the rule, of as many nations, all of whom had good opinions of themselves, and stood ready to back their pretensions.

These countries were ruled by persons who were fortunate in the selection of parents, or who, at least, were furnished with proper birth certificates.

But with her many governments and nationalities, he said, there was constant confusion. There were fear and oppression, for all these imaginary lines had to be guarded. The armies had to be kept up; the 5,000,000 soldiers must be in constant readiness for slaughter, for only by this means could the people be sufficiently impressed with the validity of the birth certificate.

Asked by the poetess Vauline, what these so-called soldiers did for a living, Mr. Oseba answered:—

"They kill folks, for, short as are the lives of the Outeroos among the superior nations, wholesale murder is the most honored of all pursuits."

Oseba said: "All the civilised nations keep these armed men, whose duty it is to kill somebody—to whom they may never have been introduced—when their ruler has a grievance, and has no time to attend to the matter himself.

"These armies, too, are potent in diplomatic controversies. When a monarch has a little misunderstanding with one of his class from a neighboring paddock, he says in deep tones:—

"'Sire, these are the facts, and if you don't believe it, Sire, look!'—and he points to his ready battalions.

"To a people who never knew of war or poverty—among whom probably not one man would care to be killed, or could find a person to accommodate him if he should, these statements seemed most amazing."

Mr. Oseba concluded, from the conspicuousness of military show, that every toiler in Europe carried a soldier on his back. And worse—he had to feed him, to clothe him, to pay him, and then to constantly submit to his insolence. From every home and fireside in Europe the most sturdy supporter, and the best loved one, was taken for target practice; and the burden imposed upon industry for showy barbarism, was crushing the whole of Europe and driving the people into revolution, anarchy and ruin.

"Tell us," said the poetess Vauline, "are you speaking of the superior, the Christian or civilised peoples?"

"Rather," said the Sage, "for only the Christian nations could enjoy, and only the superior nations could afford such heroic entertainments. As a fact, the size of the army and range of the gun are the true tests of a country's civilisation and 'superiority.'

"Strange, my children, but the 'superior' peoples, those worshipping Him who said, 'Thou shalt not kill,' have the longest guns, and the strongest battalions, and they are most ready to kill on the least provocation."

The audience, say the notes, was most impressed when told that these arguments—loaded—were aimed by the most civilised nations at each other. Oseba continues:—"The guns and the military show, help to amuse the people; they regulate home prices, and guard the dignity of the managers. They are practically the 'keep off the grass' notice; but, as a fact, my children, they are kept to-day more to overawe the people who pay the bills than to ward off any external danger.

"But there is a marked difference between the Oriental and the Occidental. The Oriental is selfish—he wants peace, and is indifferent to the fate of others. The Oriental don't care what a man believes, or what god he worships, so long as he pays the liken, and moves on; while the superior races are deeply concerned about the soul, and they want to discover all other people, and get them to join them—afterwhile.

"As social units, the Occidentals are more progressive and free, but less secure; they are more sympathetic, but less just; more interested in others, but less tolerant; and more inclined to action, and less to meditation than the Orientals.

"While there is a vast difference in the degree of oppression in Continental Europe, between class assumption, military despotism, official insolence, and creed interference, save for those for whom custom would render hell salubrious, there is no room for a liberty-loving man—especially is it no place for a people with the lofty aspirations of the Shadowas. But, oh, the poverty, the misery, the humiliating sorrow! Oh, my children! If the faith of those pretentious mortals be not folly, if there be somewhere an all-powerful God of Love and Justice, if kneeling at His throne there be hosts of saints and angels, who behold the bloody conflicts, see the widow's tears and the agonizing gasp of want; who hear the sighs of the over-worked slave, the groans of poverty and the prayers that go up to heaven from the white lips of innocence, let the Shadowas implore the masters of Europe's millions to grant mercy, or the beseeching hearts of heaven will break, and the tears of the angels will drown the world."

But, like Uphus swinging the doors to welcome the dawn of a new day, we turn to more pleasing scenes.

SCENE V.

THE BRITISH ISLES DISCOVERED.

AT this stage of the proceedings the Sage Oseba seemed to be in fine form and in most cheerful spirits.

He remarked that he was now to give his people a brief view of the "Country of Countries," an island region, just off the humming hive of uniformed Europe. Here the globe revolved until the British Isles were conspicuously in view.

"This," said Oseba, "of all the fertile dirt on the surface of Oliffa, is the most interesting. This, among the countries of the Outeroos, is the classic land of liberty, the sheet-anchor of Europe for more than three hundred years. These rock-bound Isles, with a fertile soil, a salubrious climate, indented shores—fortunately placed geographically—are by nature the best suited for the development of the ideal man of any spot on the surface of Oliffa, and having been peopled by sturdy tribes, all the suggestive hopes of Nature have been realised."

He told his people that the British Isles embraced 124,000 square miles, and contained 40,000,000 inhabitants; and that, on these few acres, there were more muscle and brain, and intellectual force and stubbornness and haughty pretension, than on any other spot of like dimensions on the surface of Oliffa.

Mount Egmont.

"These sturdy Britons, my children, who have resistlessly held these historic Islands
against all comers for many centuries, have done more to elevate, to educate, to emancipate, to civilise and to unite humanity; to free the brain from superstition, the limbs from fetters, and the world from bondage, than any other nation or race that ever inscribed its achievements on the pages of human history.

"Britain, my children, has conquered many foes, but her chief glory has been her conquests in the arts of peace. She has conquered climate, and famine, and pestilence, and the idolatry that would crucify the new upon the mouldering cross of the old régime.

"Britain has given Oliffa its industrial and commercial methods, the tone of its present civilisation, and she is rapidly giving to the whole race her erstwhile scorned language, and in this there seems a magic spell that infects all who imbibe its spirit with a burning desire for liberty. To lisp the English tongue, is to feel—a king.

"Let me tell you a little story, my children, of the most interesting, the most wonderful—yes, even the most marvellous of all the doings of man on this most erratic little planet.

"These British Isles are separated from the Continent of Europe by a damp streak, and they are inhabited by the mixed offspring of a dozen sturdy and virile tribes, all from the northern water-front. All these virile tribes, whether natives or invaders, were strongly imbued with the spirit of liberty—as they understood it. They loved peace—if they had to fight for it. They loved liberty—to squeeze the other fellow. But in the fibre of these people there was a sublime stubbornness that often made things awkward for the authorities.

"Everybody wanted to boss, so nobody would wear the collar. Everybody wanted to be free, but the feeling was so unanimous that there was abundance of officers but no privates, so it took many centuries of disputes, and quarrels, and conflicts, and wars, before they had accumulated sufficient 'grey matter' to comprehend the fact that civilised government is a compromise; that where any can be oppressed, none can be secure; and that liberty, which must halt at the gate of the other fellow's paddock, is the inalienable right of man.

"But the British can learn, and they have so well mastered this problem that the highest now yield the most ready obedience to the law, and the strongest most readily defend the rights of the weak. Though it took Britain, with her sturdy conceit, centuries to learn this, and though she, by her fibre and her position as a coloniser, was the legitimate successor of Phœnicia and Greece, she was rather backward about coming forward, for after the discovery of America, when all the other nations were madly participating in western exploits, she stood aloof for over a hundred years to complete her preparations.

"Then she came with a lunch basket, she came with both feet, she came to stay, and her achievements find no parallel in the history of human progress. Before she opened her foreign real estate office, the new world had been parcelled out. Others had staked their claims—many over-lapping—and there were plentiful notices to 'keep off the grass,' but she was undaunted.

"In 1607 she planted her first colony in America. Soon there were thirteen— an unlucky number—then she foolishly taxed them into revolt, and here she learned a valuable lesson. Since then, she has never oppressed a colony; since then, she has never taken one backward step; since then, she has gradually extended her beneficent hand over the earth, until over one-fifth of the land is painted red—her favorite hue—and over one-fourth of the human race bow a willing allegiance to her flag."

"Oh," says Leo's notes, "would not that please dear old Sir Marmaduke!"

"America, my children, of which I shall soon speak, was Britain's noblest contribution to human progress, for though the two nations have moved under different colours for more than a century, their mutual enterprise has revolutionised the industrial world, and brought humanity in touch.

"Marvel of marvels! When other nations, now in business, boasted of world-conquest, the British were but a 'handful,' inhabiting these rock-bound islands, but as mountains suggest freedom and seas adventure, looking over the waters, her daring sons went forth—not to conquer, not to exploit or to devastate, but to develop the world, and to build homes, and colonies, and states, and empires.

"If Britain took a gun in her outings—and she often did—it was to level a place for a home, a shop, or a factory. Where she plants her feet the soil becomes more fertile, and when she meets a savage, he stands more proudly erect—after the first few sermons.

"She is the motherland of America, and, by mutual efforts, the two have become the paragons of civilised progress. She saved old India from the rajahs, robbers, and priests, from famine and pestilence, and made it a paradise—as compared with its former condition. She saved strange, beloved, dreamy, half-mythical old Egypt from rot and ruin, and made it a marvel of hope and progress. She is saving 'Darkest Africa' from slavery, superstition, and fratricidal war; and, with diamonds on its golden clasps, she is handing it over to civilisation.

"She gave to civilisation Canada, with its splendid people, its fertile fields, and its stupendous 'ice-plant'; and she gave to civilisation the seven colonies of Australasia, with the most wealthy, the most commercial, the most progressive, the most advanced, educated, civilised, and free people on the whole outer surface of the planet.

"Then, to show her small respect for dirt, save as a place to fasten down upon—and her marvellous ambition for industrial development—behold! the modern commercial wonders, Hongkong and Singapore! Many nations complain of 'Britain's land-greed,' and that John Bull—as these sturdy Britons are lovingly called—always carries a bucket and a brush, and is everywhere painting the world red; but wherever the carmine shines, liberty and progress are assured. Every inch of soil wrested from darkness by British valour is handed over to civilisation—free to all comers.

"And, marvel of marvels, my children! In her more than a hundred wars— save by her mistake in striving to coerce her own children in America—she has never lost an inch of important dirt by force. And, more glorious still, every inch won from barbarism by her blood and valor, has been handed over to civilisation and human progress.

"But, no! She won much in war, which, to the infinite loss of the world, she gave back in peace.

"She took Cuba in war, restored order, and gave it back in peace. Better for the world had she kept it.

"She took by war, and gave back in peace, the Philippines, Cape Colony, Java, Sumatra, Senegal, Pondicheri, and more than twenty other valuable possessions, all to the loss of the world—and yet she has been accused of territorial avarice—of 'land hunger.'"

Right! Mr. Oseba, and had the politicians in Downing Street properly backed the sturdy British wanderers, most of Oliffa would have been painted red and done up in a shawl strap long ere this, and the Brito-Yankee race would have been in a position to guarantee peace among all nations.

"But, my children," he continued, "there are often sombre linings to many resplendent clouds, and lest you may all conclude to rush out of Cavitorus to these wonderful islands, I must show you a few of the less attractive pictures.

"Remember, that for modern civilisation among the Outeroos, the world is indebted to the colonial enterprise and success of Britain; but remember, too, that it is not always the 'colonising nations,' but the 'colonists' of the 'colonising nations,' that carry the standard of social progress to advanced grounds.

"The basis of modern colonial success, was, of course, in the fibre of the British race; but for the resistlessness of British colonial enterprise much was due to flagrant faults in Britain's domestic policy.

"We are land animals—we live on, and from the land, and Britain had but 124,000 square miles of dirt. 'Room' was scarce, so people had a 'far-away look.' But worse, a very few in the Motherland 'owned' most all this meagre surface, so people saw opportunity only in a change—for a deep love of liberty forced the evils of monopoly upon their attention.

"Well these sturdy Britons, with the mixed blood of the rugged Danes, Jutes, Celts, Saxons, Angles and others did not feel at home as guests, serfs or tenants, so they began to roam around."

The orator said he would present a few little "reasons" why the Shadowas would not care to "flock" to the British Isles, and also a review of conditions that might have had some influence in arousing the spirit of foreign adventure.

"They discovered," said he, "that of the 76,000,000 acres of dirt on the whole British Isles, one man—great only in his possessions—owned 1,350,000 acres, while another owned 460,000 acres, the two being the born owners of over 2 per cent. of the whole, upon which 40,000,000 men were compelled to live.

"They found that about two hundred families owned about half of all the land; that less than one per cent. of the people owned over 99 per cent. of the land, and that more than 90 per cent. of the people were absolutely landless.

"It is amusing, my children, to hear these sturdy British boast about 'my country,' when a few families own so much of all the land on which all must live—if they remain at home. But observing the enormous power enjoyed by the holders of vast estates in the old world, too many sought by cornering the lands, to acquire like advantages in the new, and in the correction of this ancient error, the best statesmanship of the age is still required."

Mr. Oseba proceeded to explain that as from many seemingly indefensible situations beneficent results often arise, it could hardly be doubted that the inherited curse of British landlordism has, in a most imposing "disguise," been a "blessing" to civilisation.

It impressed the thoughtful "subject" with the incomparable importance of the land to life itself, especially when population began to crowd; and it forced upon the attention, even of the thoughtless, the enormous influence and real power wielded by the possessors of large estates. The class inequalities that arose through the inheritance by the few of the source from which all must live, drove hosts of the most intelligent, sturdy, and self-reliant of the people to distant countries, and determined them to provide in the new home against the evils that had expelled them from the old.

From loathsome slime we clutch the glittering prize,
And grand results from hard conditions rise.

Waterfall, Waikaremoana.

As these emigrants loved the Motherland, they desired to remain loyal; as they had learned the advantages of land holdings, each desired to secure his own home; but remembering the past, they sought to provide that the limits of each to live from another's toil should be narrowed. Not by violating the rights of property "owners," but by securing the rights of property "creators," were new ideas popularised.

"But these inheriting world-owners," said the orator, "as a rule, have a pretty good time, though none of them have been permitted to remain long enough on their particular slice of Oliffa for it to get stale."

Reluctant to leave Britain, but anxious to pick up some of her wandering children, he closes our mother's case with this fond caress:—

"While these people of Britain are the salt of the earth, it is the offspring, and not the land-owner, who is to lead in the future social contests.

"Come to think of it, it is not 'Britain,' but the 'Briton,' that, like Atlas, carries the world on his shoulders; and 'tis the 'Briton' who is the 'salt of the earth,' while 'Britain' is the salt mine."

"DARKEST AFRICA" FINALLY DISCOVERED.

Oseba then turned his instruments on Africa. He told his audience that while along the fringe of this half-mythical land there were glimpses of a very ancient movement, the vast interior, until almost yesterday, was a veritable *terra incognito*, and to-day it is not easy to separate the grain of truth concerning its history from the cartload of fiction.

But Britain was now rolling up the sombre curtain, and opening the doors of her fabulous treasure-house that the "grateful" (?) nations might enter and take rooms.

Africa, the sage told his audience, covered one-fifth of the land surface of the outer globe, and had a population of 150,000,000 souls, or more than live in all the Americas and their islands. It has a doubtful history, thousands of years old. It was once so "civilised" that it housed three-hundred Christian Bishops, yet, to-day there is but a small portion—the Cape—that can claim more than a mere introduction to modern civilisation.

The orator informed the people, as he threw a series of pictures on the canvas, that many of the European nations were striving to extend their borders in Africa, and to the sorrow of the natives, they were now being pretty generally "discovered."

HUMAN RIGHTS.

Oh! sacred rights of man, ordained of God, yet only won by blood, and tears, and toil.

Here there was a digression, and an essay on "the rights of man," for the poetess Vauline inquired by what "right" the Europeans were "portioning out Africa," if that country had already 150,000,000 people?

"This," said the sage Oseba, as he moved his eyes from his admiring critic to his audience, "this is a pertinent question; but remember, my children, most of the inhabitants of Africa are black—they are very black."

"But is that an answer to my question?" said the poetess Vauline.

"Well," said Oseba, "it would be so deemed among the Outeroos, for questions of right and wrong do not apply to people who are unbleached."

This created great surprise, for the Shadowas had not gone entirely through the bleaching process.

"But why, among so-called civilised people, have the blacks no rights?" said the poetess Vauline.

"Plain enough," said Mr. Oseba, "for black people have no blunderbusses, and among the most civilised Outeroos 'rights' are measured by the carrying power of the guns and the skill of the men behind them. Among all the 'civilised nations' on Oliffa 'right' is measured, not by the pleadings of the master, not by the demands of humanity or justice, but in the first instance by color, for this indicates the capacity of the blunderbusses, and the nerve of the gunner.

"Yellow have rather more rights than black people, for they sometimes have a few guns and some saltpetre. 'Thou shalt not kill' and 'Thou shalt not steal' apply only to white men; and even then, only to small neighborhoods or in police affairs, for 'nations' are above these honeyed ravings, and expediency, not right, becomes the patriotic guide.

"But, my children, as John Bull is rapidly painting Africa red, we will preserve an open mind regarding that much-talked-of and little known country, though for the present it is no place for saints or Shadowas.

"I may say, in referring to colour in the discussion of questions of right, that 'red' is considerably respected. Then, too, of recent years, with improved tastes among the nations, 'red, white and blue,' thusly arranged is quite respected, while 'yellow' is very unfashionable, and 'green' is mostly admired when in uniform.

"That black Africa will, ere long, be about all red, about all British—at least in language, in sentiment, in human sympathy, in social, industrial and political methods and aspiration, if not in allegiance—can hardly be doubted; and as her ideals alone of all the races on the upper crust would satisfy us, our children may hope for further communication with these British-African colonies."

SPANISH AMERICA "DISCOVERED."

The orator here hesitated, then threw the map of what he termed "Spanish America" on the screen.

"This, my children," said he, "is Spanish America, with an area—including Central America and Mexico—of over 8,000,000 square miles, and a population of about 50,000,000 souls. This is a 'new' country, called 'new' by the Outeroos because it had been little improved since the old occupiers were blessed and sent to heaven."

The orator claimed that, in forest, in soil, in mineral wealth, and in all the resources of Nature necessary to the subsistence of a great population, South was probably superior to North America; yet, behold the mighty difference! The world had never presented so conspicuous an opportunity for weighing the merits of different races as colonisers and civilisers as are shown in the present conditions of South and North America, and all these marvellous disparities lie in the character of the invading or colonising races.

North America sprang from the loins of Britain; South, from the loins of Spain. That tells the story. But a comparison in all the late colonial enterprises of the world, shows Britain to hold an equally favorable position, for of all the "foreign" dependencies of all the other nations of the globe, there is not one that enjoys a sufficient degree of liberty and social progress to render it self-supporting—possibly, save Java, held by the Dutch.

The 50,000,000 Spanish-Americans, he observes, write less than one-half the number of letters written by 5,000,000 Canadians, and they have less commerce than 4,500,000 Australians, and less newspapers than 800,000 New Zealanders—and education and commerce means civilisation.

A TEMPEST.

Here the sage amusingly described a Spanish-American revolution.

He said:—

"When the young men of any city become weary with the more common excitements, the theatre and the bullfight, they organise a 'revolution.' For this 'outing' they call together their friends, arm themselves, establish a camp on the outlying hills, and make ready for 'slaughter.' The 'loyalists'—salaried clerks usually, with a few hangers-on—rush out to meet the belligerents, and approach to within a reasonably safe distance, when both sides 'fall in,' fire simultaneously—each over the others' heads—when all break and run for the treasury.

"If the 'loyalists' win the race they vote themselves extra pay, smoke a cigar, and enjoy a *siesta*; while if the others win, the treasury is looted, a new set of clerks installed, the taxes are raised to repair the damages, and the new 'push' enjoy the *siesta*.

"The security of the public from too frequent changes rests in the fact that usually the camp of the 'loyalists' is taken up between that of the insurgents and the treasury, so the 'loyalists' have a shorter run to make in the home stretch.

"Think, my children, what civilisation would have been to-day had the British been content to remain on their Island home, or had both the Americas been permanently held by the Spanish race—or, to judge by later history, by any other than the Anglo-Saxon.

"Well, my friends, I have no interest in booming any country, but if I had owned all Spanish-America in 'fee simple,' and had a long lease on Hades, I would rent my freehold out, and reside on my other holding."

(Leo remarks:—"Oh, for a laugh with Sir Marmaduke.")

"No," said the sage, "there is nothing worthy of imitation in Spanish-America, and there is no room under the present rule in these countries for the staid virtues of the Shadowas."

SCENE VI.

AMERICA "DISCOVERED."

OSEBA said he was now to return to rather favourite pastures. He was now to review the situation of a country unanimously admitted, by all its millions of proud and patriotic people, to be the "greatest country," not only on this earth, but in the Universe—and this, of course, meant America.

Leo Bergin, having been born in America, seemed to be "at home" to these graceful compliments.

Oseba said that before he reached America, that country had been somewhat "discovered" by a Mr. Morgan, who had much of it done up in a shawl strap, but that it was still considerably in business.

This American nation, he said, sprang from the loins of Britain, and its founders had inherited their fibre from that "classic land of liberty." Being strongly imbued with the British spirit, and being impressed by their novel surroundings, they broke the thread of tradition, and, having established a government based upon the consent of the governed, they demonstrated the possibility of a civilised state without a king or a bishop.

Here the orator grew eloquent, "as if to the manner born," and I quote:—

"America—North America—is the noblest country ever given by God to his children—a country saved through all the progressive ages of the world for a new experiment in human government, and here some British adventurers opened a branch office. That they might 'worship God according to the dictates of their own conscience,' they hurled themselves in their frail barques, turned their prows—the ships' prows—to three thousand miles of boisterous waves, and landed on Plymouth's rock-bound shores. Here, defying titanic difficulties, they scaled the mountains, levelled the forests, tamed the soil, and, from the jaws of many defeats, they snatched a glorious victory. Here, they erected new altars, blazed out a new destiny, and, rocked in the cradle of Liberty by the untrammelled winds of heaven, they built a temple at whose shrines the unborn generations could freely worship."

Here, the notes record that a young man in the audience smiled, while poetess Vauline seemed good-naturedly surprised; noticing which, Amoora Oseba faltered, and said:—

"Well, my children, those remarks would be very tame in America, and a man who could not soar higher on a 'fitting occasion' would certainly not be returned at the head of the poll."

But in material prosperity, the orator said that during the first century of America's national life, she achieved not only unparalleled, but unapproached success, and during the last half of that period she accumulated more wealth than was ever possessed by any other nation. With nearly half of the railways of the globe, she furnished half the food and raiment products, and manufactured more goods than any other four nations—aside from Britain—and by the brightest inventive genius the world ever knew, she had furnished more of the cunning devices that ease the care and toil of man, than all the world besides.

Queenstown, The Remarkables in the distance.

In moral progress, she has been equally successful, for she had about two-fifths of all the newspapers of the world; 72,000 post offices, 180,000 churches, 450,000 school teachers, and more libraries and more readers than any other country; while more than half of the institutions of higher learning on the globe were hers, and counting only the real Americans, more enterprising, ingenious, intelligent and educated people, than any other nation.

"Verily," said Oseba, "America was Britain's greatest contribution to the world's progress. These two kindred countries flourished through reciprocal interests; by their industrial methods they have lifted the world from medieval barbarism, and they are destined to give their language, their civilisation and their notions of liberty to the whole human race."

Here the poetess Vauline inquired why America, with all her great wealth and opportunities, would not be a desirable country to which to send a colony of the Shadowas?

"A cloud was on his brow."

Oseba answered, "I love that great and wonderful country so deeply, and I so much admire its splendid audacity, that I would gladly speak kindly, even of its faults; but, my children, it is not all 'rosewater and glycerine' in Yankeedom.

"In wealth, in enterprise, in education, in intelligence, and in opportunities for further progress, America may justly claim to be the foremost nation on the globe, and she has 'rights' no other would care to dispute. But,—

'The people, Oh! the people,
Those much lower than the steeple.'

It is they, of whom we may profitably inquire. A nation may be rich, though the people may be poor; a nation may be strong, while the people are weak; a nation may be feared because the people can be relied upon to obey designing masters, but the true greatness of a nation must ever depend upon the quality of the individuals composing the nation.

"In America, my children, they sing many choruses. Listening across the sea, the groans of despair are heard, mingled with the inspiring chants of robed priests, and, the public heart being touched with pity, the bandmaster mounts his pedestal, looks serenely benevolent, and, raising his baton with gracefully curving signals, the populace join in one voice:—

'Come, ye, from lands oppressed,
Come, ye, from east and west,
Come, join our happy throng,
Come, join in joyous song,—
For in this goodly land, nor want, nor poor,
No kings oppress, no beggars seek the door.
In Plenty's beauteous lap we wile the days away,
Come, 'walk into our trap'—why need you long delay?'

"These dulcet tones were always supposed to help fill the immigrant ships, the vacancies caused by the strike, and the land-boomer's pockets, but just as the last faint echoes die away, there arises from the narrow lane 'hard by'— just off Broadway—the plaintive wail:—

'Do ye hear the children weeping, O my brothers,
E'er the sorrow comes with years?
They are leaning their young heads against their mothers,
And *that* cannot stop their tears.
The young lambs are bleating in the meadows,
The young birds are chirping in the nest,

The young fawns are playing with the shadows,
The young flowers are blowing toward the West,—
But the young, young children, O my brothers,
They are weeping bitterly!
They are weeping in the playtime of the others,
In the country of the free.'

"Of course, my children, these borrowed lamentations may come from the fellows who were left out in the cold at the last elections, for one 'can't most always sometimes tell,' in America, whence come the inspiring motives of the entertainment.

"Let me tell you a little story, my children.

"One November afternoon, while on a west-bound train, I had as a travelling companion a very intelligent, patriotic, and sorrowful man. His manner was subdued, his voice was plaintive, and he spoke earnestly of the condition of his country.

"Skipping his most emphatic words, and toning down portions of his most lurid sentences, I will recite to you the substance of his fervid oration as we hurried over the plains to overtake the rapidly sinking sun.

"Speaking of the greatness of America, my friend said, 'Some qualifying words may be necessary, or the ideas sought to be conveyed may be confusing. We Americans,' said he, 'boast of "equality before the law," yet in no other civilised country has favoritism been carried to more deplorable extremes. We boast of freedom, yet in no country does a smaller number of men control the conditions under which all must live, and we boast of our constitutionally guarded rights, yet the accidental head of a party may exercise a power unthinkable by any constitutional monarch of Europe.'

"'But with so intelligent a people, may not these abuses be remedied?'

"'Intelligent?' said he, with a sigh. 'The people in America are frequently informed that they are very intelligent and free, but would a very intelligent people shovel coal so furiously into the furnace of a locomotive that was rapidly running their train to the devil?'

"'In theory, the Americans have erected the most symmetrical political temple, at whose altars the devout head of patriotism ever bowed a humble allegiance; but in practice,' said he with emotion, 'well, the upper rooms are occupied by schemers and the halls are crowded by a more rapacious set of money-changers than the Master whipped from the temple of Jerusalem.'

"'Dollars, dollars,' said he bitterly, 'there is nothing in America more potent than a million dollars.' Then after a moment's silence he muttered, 'yes, five millions are more potent.'

"'However, it would be mockingly absurd,' he sorrowfully continued, 'for any American to hoist a danger signal, for the pleasures of the occasion must not be marred; but,' said he, with a gleam of satisfaction, 'while Belshazzar is playing high jinks at the feast, Daniel is changing his slippers, making ready for a call. As a fact,' said my companion, 'America is being looted by her caretakers, and, while the Philistines are packing away the booty, the silly Samsons are sleeping in the lap of Delilah.'

"My friend was eloquent and impressive—his language was lurid and expressive, his manner was quite American, and I sympathised with him, for 'tis sad to behold the patriot, sitting with bowed head and solemn visage, contemplating the waning glory of his own proud country, and he seemed very earnest.

"Well," said Oseba, "we pulled up at a pretty city where there was confusion, and my friend disenrailed. As he stepped off, he met some friends. They, too, looked unhappy, and, feeling inquisitive, I alighted, and observing a pleasant looking fellow on the platform I approached him, and waving toward my late companion's party, I interrogatively said: 'Funeral?'

"The man actually laughed, and observing my seriousness, and that I was not of his country, he laughed again, and glancing at my friend's group, he said:—

"'Funeral, stranger! We've had an election, and it was the d——st landslide ever seen in these parts, and he—ha! ha!—is out in the cold.'"

Oseba, the notes say, remarked that the bell rang, he "waved" to his companion, re-entered his train, dropped into his seat and—thought.

A DIGRESSION.

The notes indicate that Mr. Oseba was deeply affected by the revelations of his "travelling companion." He need not despair.

This race has been rather prominently before the footlights for some time, and it is of such a mixed and sturdy stock that it seems endowed with the spirit, if not of "perpetual," at least, of long-continued youth.

The Anglo-Saxon has not yet filled his mission, and surely America should not, so early in its unparalleled career, betray evidence of decadence. While "grow quick, decay quick," seems to be a law of nations, as well as of Nature, while wealth is often an evidence of injustice, and while in numbers there are often germs of weakness, with America still in her vigorous youth, there must be virtue in her strength sufficient to meet these very apparent difficulties.

It must be remembered, too, that America, though she had great opportunities, had a stupendous task before her at her birth as a nation. In vindication of an inherited British instinct, the "British colonies" revolted against a king, too Dutch to appreciate a British sentiment, and a parliament, too weak to resist him, and the "British American" colonies became the "American nation."

But the responsibilities of the new nation were as tremendous as her opportunities were fabulous. Politically, she was adrift without pilot or compass, and she set about to erect a temple on whose altars her people might worship, and, without law or precedent, she built, better than she knew, a theory of government the astonishment, the pride, and the admiration of a hopeful world.

Well might the heads of the people have been a little turned, but lured by the most tempting opportunities ever offered to man, they hurled an awakened energy against the doors of the treasure house of Nature, and soon marched among the leaders of industrial art—yes, away in the vanguard. In defence of her commerce, her little navy was the first to humble the Barbary pirates that for centuries had levied blackmail upon the whole Mediterranean trade. Her flag was soon seen in every port, and from the profits of trade in her products, Britain laid the foundation of a stupendous industrial system, that made her the commercial mistress of the world.

Her pursuits were industrial, her ways were ways of peace. Soon she carried one-third of the ocean tonnage, and the struggles of the whole human race were being eased by her inventions.

During these formative stages of development, real poverty was unknown, and great fortunes—such as are being heaped up to-day—had never been dreamed of.

But what a period, and what a country for the development of character! In those peaceful but industrious and frugal days arose that splendid school of writers, poets, essayists, philosophers, publicists and reformers of New England, and the orators, statesmen, and patriots of the young days of the Republic. With such achievements, Mr. Oseba, liberty cannot perish from the earth. The grotesque anomalies in America are incidents of the changing times and will soon disappear.

But to the notes:—

"Room for a colony? Quantity, my children, but no tempting quality for us.

"No," said Oseba, "earnestly I love America and her splendid people, but the flag of social progress has been transferred to other lands, so America must hold the 'phone, while others of that splendid race—more strays from the Classic Isles—answer the calls of Justice and lead Humanity to a broader, higher and nobler liberty.

"Well, I will ring off America, for while every phase of the recital is so charming that one is inclined to loiter, we catch a glimpse of coming scenes that hurry our hopes for a pleasing goal.

"From great and grand America, I took a long ocean voyage, my children, and on the 'other side' I found the beginning of the end of my task, for here, all the dreams of all my weary wanderings, and all the hopes of all my fancied visions of better things, found realisation, and with a glad heart I turned my thoughts to the friends of Cavitorus."

The Lion Rock, 5000ft. high, Milford Sound

SCENE VII.

AUSTRALASIA DISCOVERED.

And they sent ships to distant lands, and brought gold, and copper, and fine wool, and the merchants made much gains.

AT this juncture the loved and lost Leo Bergin notes a short intermission, for, as there is everywhere a limit to human endurance, Oseba had grown weary.

During the recess, the notes inform us, there were many whisperings, many doubtful shakes of the head, and many real fears expressed as to results regarding the conclusions of the report.

"We have gone over the globe," said a learned-looking matron, "and we have no encouragement."

"Better know the truth," said another.

"It is a matter of no small importance to Cavitorus," said a third.

The people stood, or sat, in groups and conversed earnestly, some consulting a small globe which stood on the edge of the rostrum. At the expiration of an hour, the people resumed their seats, Amoora Oseba took the platform, and the audience was all attention.

When he arose, he told the people that he understood their feelings, their hopes, their fears, and their anxieties. He had done his best, and his devoted comrades had been as solicitous as he for their beloved country and its cause. To err is human, but it were better to be over-cautious than over-anxious for a change. Not all changes mean progress, though this is not always understood, even by the world leaders.

He told his audience they were not finished—Oliffa had not yet been wholly reported upon, for they had made other discoveries. There were yet two countries to inspect, and he bid them be of good cheer. He said the countries to which he was now to call attention were quite "new" in the sense that they had been known, even to the Outeroos themselves, but a comparatively short time. He then turned on the light, exposed the full globe, and proceeded:—

"The earth has practically been circumnavigated, and, when you have seen all, I hope you will be satisfied with my efforts.

"We have visited all countries inhabited by man, and my discoveries have revealed many interesting facts, suggesting many conclusions.

"Mankind," argued Mr. Oseba, "is akin. All sorts and conditions of men emerged from a common ancestry. The vast differences in form, color, language, custom and mentality have been caused by the varied environing conditions slowly working throughout many ages. From common passions, common wants and common efforts for their gratification, has man slowly pressed forward, the pace varying as Nature invited or forbade the movement.

"But genius has annihilated time and space. The world is being brought in touch, and the race that improved the cunning of the hand, and aroused the inquiry of the brain, is destined to guide, unify, and dominate the world.

"The Anglo-Saxon is a peculiar compound of many mixed and sturdy tribes, and in the genius of race, there is the magic potion that is giving tone, language and inspiration to humanity.

"But the modern Briton is the finished product of Anglo-Saxon aims, and inherited aspiration. The Briton is a trinity composed of English, Irish and Scotch, a compound of the most stubborn vices and most sturdy virtues ever found in an organised society.

"Janus was not a Briton; the Briton has but one face, and it is always looking to the front. The Briton is sturdy, so he presses forward; he is weary, and he never runs; he is tenacious, and he appropriates everything having one loose end. Having more wants than industry, he invents that he may be satisfied. He adjusts himself to new conditions, so he hoists his flag over his new cabin and annexes all in sight. Being dull as a linguist, the people of all climes have to learn his speech, or abstain from the banquet of the present, and—the future.

"Yes, the British are of a sturdy race. They were developed in a fine climate. But people can't live on climate, and these people had appetites. No *thing* can come from nothing. Thoughts and actions are 'products,' but the finished goods always reveal the character of the raw material. Strange," he argued, "but as a man eats, so is he. The Frenchman eats frog, and he dances; the Italian eats macaroni and he runs a hand organ; while the Briton as a regular diet takes beef-steak and lion, so he wanders about, and—paints the world red.

"In less time than it took the old nations to build a city, the inhabitants of the small British Isles had pre-empted more than one-fifth of the surface of the planet, and were masters of the affections of a fourth of the human race. But the noblest works accomplished by this resistless people are now to be revealed, for the admiration of my countrymen."

Here he turned on the great forty-foot sphere to an axial angle of twenty-three degrees, well exposing the Southern Hemisphere. After noticing the southern orifice—the back door of Symmes' Hole—and the difference in the distribution of land and water near the respective poles, he turned the globe so as to give a fair exposure of Australasia.

In Oseba's more cheerful demeanor, his more ready speech, and his radiant countenance, there was a gleam of joy, and when once the full import of this new scene was appreciated, there was a generous burst of applause—Leo notes, "almost enthusiasm."

"This," said the sage Oseba, "is the 'Austral climes,' the last dry dirt on the surface of Oliffa, wholly rescued from darkness and devoted to civilisation.

"Its color indicates its social condition—it is civilised and free, for on Oliffa, my children, 'red' is the emblem of hope. 'Painting the world red,' means turning on the light, and John Bull always carries a bucket of carmine—and he often has a 'brush.'"

Oseba said that in the whole inquiry he had endeavoured to follow an example set, many centuries ago, by a Personage whose advice is constantly quoted on Oliffa—and more constantly ignored—of keeping the best to the last.

Australia was of old called an island, but as in area it about equalled the United States of America, and almost that of Europe—having near 3,000,000 square miles—it was now regarded as a "continent," though it had less than 4,000,000 people.

"Room for a colony?" said the poetess Vauline, with something bordering emotion.

"Yes," said Oseba.

But let us proceed cautiously. I boil down.

He said there was plenty of "room," and for sometime there would be "room to let," but as a fact, while a lovely land, inhabited by a splendid people, it was not quite all it seemed on the map. On the borders of the "Australian continent," and reaching back long hundreds of miles, there was much beautiful country, but there was a vast interior, which, though red on the map, was almost too thin even to hold the paint.

As a fact, much of the surface of Australia was afflicted, like many of her people, with an insatiable thirst. To the uninformed, this "dry" and hot interior gave Australia a "bad name," as people are usually influenced by "sound," and they rarely stop to reflect how many grand empires might be carved out from these fertile borders and plains.

He described how Cook "found" Australia in 1770, and how, by the directions of Sydney, Colonial Secretary, it was first "colonised" in 1779. He recorded its struggles and growth during the silent years; how colonial authority was exercised; how self rule, or so-called "responsible government" was established; and how, to reach more remote portions of the country from convenient seats of authority, several autonomous colonies were formed.

Owing to the large expense of coming, immigrants were usually of the better class; and, owing to the distance from central authority, the colonist became self-reliant, and soon began to apply new ideas to new conditions.

He dwelt with evident pleasure upon the development of the cities of the continental colonies as splendid centres of wealth and population, and praised the spirit that was ready to cast tradition to the winds, and boldly experiment upon various expedients, that seemed a solution for some pressing problem.

In describing Australasian cities, he declared that Sydney was the most beautiful city on earth, having a society which, for culture and character, equalled that of any other country. He admired the competitive spirit as between the different or several political centres, and of the many departures from old notions.

The courage of the people in the adoption of new political methods, and their re-arrangement of the relations between governments and industrial forces, seemed to please him greatly.

He declared that "these self-governing autonomous colonies, aroused by inviting opportunities of a novel environment, inspired by a sphere of undefined liberty, with reckless readiness to resort to new expedients for the accomplishment of new purposes, had produced in Australasia, in all the essentials of true worth, the highest average type of man and womanhood on the surface of Oliffa—with the more isolated New Zealand probably leading."

Oseba said the Australasians enjoyed a higher average plane of living than any other people; they were better educated, better clothed, better fed, and better housed, and, with comparisons made on the same or like basis, they were the greatest commercial people on the globe, with proportionately much greater banking power than any other people. In proportion to population, these 4,500,000 Australasians had four times the capital of the people of other leading countries, and their commerce was four times larger.

He applauded the tendency towards holding the lands at nominal or low rents for the use of the people; the construction, ownership and management of the railways, telegraphs, telephones and other public utilities, by the government for the convenience and use of the governed, as the acme of political wisdom.

He claimed that the Australasians had confirmed every lesson of history, for all experience taught that only through colonial enterprise were experiments in legislation safe, and advanced ideas crystallised into law. Small communities might safely experiment, and when the people bore sway, the dangers possible from rapid changes were preferable to the mildew of stagnation.

In political and social progress, in material prosperity and moral worth, the people of Australasia were conspicuously at the head of the procession.

Only through the influence of colonial enterprise, had real liberty ever gained a substantial victory, and only through expedients suggested by colonial necessities, had great economic changes hurriedly come.

America, in her free and fearless youth, far excelled the motherland in liberal legislation and economic progress, but the millstone of aggregated wealth and "vested interests" weighed her down, and she retired from the leadership, while Australasia, with her novel surroundings and the experience of all the former ages to contemplate, proposed to sail a little further over the inviting seas of social progress, and her success had vindicated the wisdom of her determination. At a time when many other nations were almost madly pushing colonial experiments, she had written a new volume corroborating the evidence of the centuries, that Britain alone, of all modern nations, possessed the requisite qualities for successful colonisation.

"Australasia deserves well of the world," said Oseba, "for under the separate standards of her many colonial chiefs, she has moved the people on to a most advanced position.

Looking down the Mueller Glacier from Ball Pass, Mount Cook.

"But in Australia proper there has recently come a change that must necessarily check the rapidity of Australian progress. Six of the Australasian colonies—New Zealand not joining—have left the skirmish-line, and formed into a less mobile mass. The light infantry have buckled on heavy knapsacks—the flying artillery have been re-cast into siege guns. The 'states' are now anchored to the past, and the 'Commonwealth' must be unwieldy. The members of this compact may chafe, but the chains are unyielding, and the ponderous hulk, in which all the luggage has been tossed, will be found cumbrously slow in its movements.

"As social groups, the Australians, in their 'free colonies,' were in their vigorous youth—they were buoyant and ambitious. They looked abroad, beheld what others had done, and said, 'Let us take another step,' and being free and self-ruling, they were able to hurriedly adjust their political machine to their local requirements.

"Inspired by novel environments, great opportunities and hard necessities, the Phœnicians and the Greeks, as colonisers, gave to Europe its commercial instincts; and, inspired by like opportunities and necessities, the British have not only made the dreams of the ancients a reality but they have created and firmly established modern civilisation. America is the Carthage of Phœnicia. Australasia is the *Magna Grecia* of Greece. Australia has played well her part.

"But a new king has come, my children, 'who knew not Joseph,' and no Moses can lead the people rapidly out from the shadow of the 'Commonwealth.'

"Australia has a genial climate; she has broad, fertile acres enough to support a grand empire; she has a magnificent people, and she has advanced the standard of social progress many a league, but a 'tribal' exuberance has been hampered by allegiance to a central authority, so the leadership in social progress must be passed to less incumbered hands.

"The world stands in mute admiration at Australia's social achievements; but, to gratify the ambition of a few men who desired a broader field for the display of a splendid talent, she has lost her 'innings,' and 'New Zealand' has the bat.

"When the Commonwealth band struck up, it was whispered across 1,200 miles of sea to New Zealand, 'Will you walk into my parlor?' but the sturdy Seddon answered, 'No, thanks! we will go ahead, and turn on a little more light.'

"Then, while I love the Australians and shall ever hope for their future prosperity, we will 'ring off,' and review the last, the loveliest, and the most free and inviting field ever explored by man, for already the colors are in worthy hands, and the leaders have proposed to take another step."

Summing up for a conclusion, the sage Oseba said that China, even with "opportunities," presented no varieties; and while Japan had variety, she had no room. Europe was too strongly wedded to militarism for healthy mental growth; Britain has become a park for her nobles; Africa had the black plague; America was owned by the trusts, and was managed in their interests by the party bosses; and Australia, like a child crying for bracelets, had put on hand-cuffs.

"So, none of these answer the requirements of our commission," said the orator, "and I now invite you, my children, to another series of pictures in our elaborate gallery—'tis of my last 'discovery.'"

Here, pending the re-adjustment of the instruments, the audience indulged in a few moments of lively conversation, for the promises seemed to be more encouraging. But soon Mr. Oseba stepped to the front with a confident dignity, and in a pleasing voice said:—

"My learned colleagues, and you, my beloved countrymen and women, I have detained you long, and, that you might appreciate my conclusions, I have gone somewhat into details in my extensive review. I have shown you many of my discoveries, on the outer surface of our planet; I have explained the political systems of many peoples, and I have observed the play of your emotions as the conditions of men were portrayed; but I now promise you only pleasing revelations, for in beauty, in climate, in soil and social situation, I am going to show you the paradise of Oliffa, and this means a portion of Australasia that declined to join the federation of which I have spoken—it means New Zealand, on the map, 'Zealandia,' with the poets, but Zelania, as it would be called in our more musical speech, and by this euphonious title shall we speak of that charming land. This, my children, was my last discovery, and while many people on Oliffa don't care to be discovered at all, I hope the 'Zelanians' will never regret my having landed on their blissful shores."

SCENE VIII.—Act I.

ZELANIA—MR. OSEBA'S LAST DISCOVERY.

BLUE pencilling several eloquent pages, I am here constrained to use the discretion generously given me, by choosing for myself the methods of introducing the scenes of Mr. Oseba's last discovery.

Hinemoa's Bath, of Legendary Fame

It has been previously mentioned that Leo Bergin had "done newspaper work in New Zealand," and here seems a proper place to re-refer to this pleasing fact.

Leo notes that, pending a re-arrangement of the stage, there was a brief intermission, and later, that having become weary from strained attention, and drowsy from the soothing pleasures of the occasion, his thoughts flitted back over the silent years, and falling into a half-unconscious reverie, he seized the thread and wove from the thrilling scenes of the past the panorama of a pleasing dream. In his chant, we catch the echoes of a farewell to his native land, and, floating away into aimless realms, he follows the devious path of other days, where vaguely arise the fleeting phantoms of pleasures forever gone.

We know not the mystery of a dream, but in Leo Bergin's brain the hoary mountains rise, the restless seas moan, and the scenes of ever-enchanting

Zelania unroll like a magic scroll. In modest phrase he sings the memories of early wanderings, and that through his mental gleams we may reach a higher appreciation of the unfolding views, I quote his rippling rhymes:—

LEO BERGIN'S REVERIE.

SWEET home, adieu! With vent'rous crew,
I'm sailing o'er the ocean blue.

AS on we leap, the eye doth sweep
The curving borders of the deep.

THE days glide by, I gaze and sigh,
But nought appears, save sea and sky.

BEHOLD! there rise, 'neath Southern skies,
Green Isles that greet our glad surprise.

OH! lovely Isles, where Nature smiles,
And beckons to the "afterwhiles."

HERE fancy drew, from old and new,
To give the soul extended view.

WITH air so mild, and scenery wild,
The Fates persuaded, led and smiled.

O! CRAGGY peak! O! Earthquakes freak,
Had I but words of you to speak.

OUR course we take, through broom and brake,
To view the fern-embroidered lake.

THOSE lakes, so sweet, at mountain's feet,
Where weary strangers, strangers meet.

THE waters blue, with swift canoe,
We skim, for glimpses weird and new.

WE lift the eye to mountain high,
To where the snow-peaks kiss the sky.

O'ER gorges deep, where shadows creep,
dark clouds cluster, pause and weep.

IN dreamy mood, we pause and brood,
'Midst awe-inspiring solitude.

WE list—a roar, that cometh o'er,
From danger scenes we would explore.

FOR ah! the spell! the geyser's well,
That hurls the sulphurous fumes from hell;

THAT flings on high, with thund'rous sigh,
Huge rocks, that smite the cloud-flecked sky.

BUT list, ye bands from other lands,
This monument of splendor stands,

IN South Seas hurled, with flag unfurled,
"The scenic wonder of the world."

AS here we scan old Nature's plan,
We seek her last, best work—a man.

LO! he appears! nor hopes nor fears
Have vexed his soul through all the years.

WITH haughty pride—nor priest nor guide—
He ruled the land, as warrior tried.

HERE chieftain brave, here King and slave,
Their lives to war and foray gave.

HERE, dusky maid was ne'er afraid
To join the fray, in copse or glade.

WITH waving hair, and beauty rare,
Brave hearts these maidens did ensnare.

WHEN beauty wild a chief beguiled,
He gazed in liquid eyes, and smiled.

LOVE makes amends, and often blends,
Wild warring factions into friends.

BUT strong the will, with tribesmen's skill,
The Maori was unconquered still.

WHERE Nature, kind, unfolds the mind,
Man is to nobler thoughts inclined.

THOUGH brave, he's meek; he aids the weak,
And high companionship doth seek.

IN social train, by hand and brain,
He wins and holds a vast domain.

HE builds a State; 'tis weak or great,
As based on love, or fosters hate.

IF Wisdom's eyes survey the skies,
Before their magic touch arise

INDUSTRIAL arts, where loyal hearts
May rear and fill commercial marts.

IF strong and just, and true to trust,
The coin of Truth can never rust;

AND wise men see that none are free,
Save where there's large equality—

WHERE Law commands, that sturdy hands,
Shall freely cultivate the lands;

NO coward slave, but free and brave,
Shall ever ready be to save.

THUS honest worth, o'er all the earth,
Conditions make, e'en more than birth.

'TWAS said by Fate, these Isles must wait,
The builders of an ideal State.

THEN with the breeze, 'cross Southern seas,
The Briton came, with high decrees.

NEW scenes arose, old wounds they close,
And friendship reigns 'mong ancient foes.

FOR Maori hate, by skill and—"fate"—
Was merged into the British "State."

UNITED, free, they now agree
To dwell in peace,—"So mote it be."

THEN of this man, and if we can,
We'll follow out his mystic plan.

FOR wise it seems, e'en in our dreams,
To build, with care, prophetic themes.

THEN let us gauge the Seer and Sage,
As pass they o'er Life's mystic stage.

FIRST, of the dead, it may be said,
While warm of heart and cool of head,

THEY saw the new, and though but few,
They laid foundations, strong and true,

ON which to rear, without a fear,
This temple,—so imposing here.

BY words sublime, in prose and rhyme,
They taught, for all-enduring time.

THEN Seddon came, without whose name
This temple were unfinished frame.

BUT in his care, with graceful air,
The structure rose, with finish fair.

HIS sturdy stroke the times awoke,
As from Tradition's rules he broke.

UPON the land he scattered bands,
With willing hearts and sturdy hands.

TO those once rent with discontent,
He even-handed Justice sent.

NOW o'er the State, nor fear nor hate
Could find companion, small or great.

LOOK o'er the land, from peak to strand,
There's happiness on every hand.

HERE Cities rare, exceeding fair,
Zealania boasts, with modest air.

AT eve or dawn, we gaze upon
The busy, "blowy" Wellington.

HERE, products great for ships await,
And here repose the powers of State.

HERE, founding laws, for mighty cause,
The statesman long the session draws.

HERE modest worth and homely mirth
Find more respect than rank or birth.

THERE'S Auckland, too—'twixt me and you—
A beauty spot, excelled by few.

ROUND this fair cove, old Nature strove
To show the fickle feats of Jove.

VOLCANIC smoke in fury broke,
Until the heavens all awoke.

WHEN cleared the skies, there did arise
A seat for earthly Paradise.

AT mountains' feet, where lavas meet,
There Auckland sits, serene and sweet.

WITH seas afore, just off her door,
Where proud ships ride for evermore.

WE note with care, with Christchurch, there
Are few that safely may compare.

FOR pride of race, for social grace,
She holds a high and honored place.

'MID fertile plain of waving grain,
We search for lovelier spot, in vain.

HERE, soul and brain; here, maid and swain,
A pure companionship maintain.

DUNEDIN stands, on favored lands,
'Twixt mountains high and ocean sands.

ON beauty's spot, the "Canny Scot"
Has cast his ever happy lot.

WITH taste and skill, from rock to rill,
Dunedin reaches 'long the hill.

WITH vision free—upon the lee—
Dunedin gazes o'er the sea.

FULL many more, 'tween hill and shore,
Are worthy of the poet's lore.

THOUGH hard I seek, the words are weak,
Of nobler beauties now to speak.

WHILE cities were, with beauty rare,
Contrived by man, with studied care,

THE vale, the glen, the lake, the fen,
Were made by Him who maketh men.

THE fields of grain, where honest swain
Earns honest bread, wave not in vain.

FOR West and East, both man and beast
Await to join Zealania's feast.

AND from all lands, by skilful hands,
White sails are bent for Austral strands.

HERE, finest wheat, by many a fleet
Is sent, the foreign marts to meet.

AND finest fleece—in war or peace—
They shear, that wealth they may increase.

WITH choicest meat, both rare and sweet,
In "Merry England," they compete.

IN farm or mine, with food or wine,
To lead the leaders they incline.

BY skill they coil the threads of toil
Around the riches of the soil.

AND, for the sake of gain to make,
Great enterprise they undertake.

WELL, far and near, we've gathered here,
And all in all it doth appear

THAT higher goals and nobler souls
Are here, than elsewhere 'tween the poles.

NOW wake, my Muse, do not refuse
To pay "my hostess" honest dues.

FOR ladies fair, with beauty rare,
Zealania boasts, beyond compare.

AND smiles more sweet we'll never meet
Until we bow at Peter's feet.

AWAKE again and listen, when
Beholding strong Zealania's men.

'TIS writ by Fate, men only great
Could constitute this noble State.

THEN sing for all, both great and small,
Each in fit place, that none may fall.

THE dreams of seers, the hopes and fears,
Have gathered 'long the silent years,

AND on these Isles, with radiant smiles,
Were cast the hoarded "afterwhiles."

ZEALANIA fair, thou art the heir
Of all the cries of ancient prayer.

HERE sturdy bands, with gen'rous hands,
Are guardians of these favored lands.

THEN hail thee thrice—let this suffice,
Thou art Creation's Paradise.

OH! float away—like mist in May,
Or rainbow tints 'mid ocean spray.

"I WAKE to sense—please, no offence,—
Forgive my drowsy indolence."

Well, indeed that is pretty; but let us down from Leo's fancies to Mr. Oseba's facts, and while I shall strive to retain a seasoning of Mr. Oseba's richness, time and the love of ease whisper persuasively of the virtues of the blue pencil.

With more animated eloquence, Mr. Oseba resumed his oration. "The audience," says Leo Bergin, "gave the most profound attention."

"Knowledge," said Mr. Oseba, "is a priceless treasure, but," with a smile he continued, "many a good story has been spoiled by over-inquisitiveness.

Poetic fancy suffers from flirtations with cause and conscience. Unless inquiry has been thorough, my children, it is wiser, in most cases, to note impressions than to assume to record facts, so I shall give you but a 'bird's-eye' view of these enchanting isles, with the characters as they appeared before the visual camera when I made my observations.

"Had I gone fossicking among the weary ones of Zelania, I should doubtless have found many excellent people who, in some phase of the inquiry, would have questioned the correctness of my conclusions. I might have heard some sighs, amid the almost universal joy—some smiles with the general congratulations, and some discordant groans mingled with the generous applause—but where there is not sufficient diversity of interest to produce mental friction, there is more danger from decomposition than from revolution.

"Yes, I incline to think had I stood on the corner and listened I would have met some well-to-do gentlemen who disliked the land tax; some business men who disliked the labor laws; some farmers, who wanted a free ride and no rent; some patriotic men who failed to admire many of 'Richard's' taking ways. I might also have found healthy gentlemen from 'Home' who, though their conditions were bettered by coming, have little love for 'the colonials,' and who, by virtue of their unwillingness to grasp the true situation, regard every statement of a fact as an extravagance, and every forward movement as a revolution. Then, I should have felt it necessary to inquire how much of such criticism was due to private interest, to defeated ambition, to party or factional prejudice, or to differences in opinion as to who would best grace the conspicuous chair.

"For this I had neither time nor inclination. Man can equivocate, can even lie, 'tis said, but visible conditions never deceive an observing stranger, and when I considered the brief history of that country and compared its early social and political policy with the present free, happy and prosperous situation, I had little care to banquet with private grievance or public criticism.

"I was concerned, not in the salaries of the public servants, but in the character of the public conscience; not in who, for the time being, guided the ship of state, but how the passengers and the crew were being brought to their destination.

"On a lonely elevation, far removed from the murmuring crowd, I levelled my glass, and, without sampling the fluids from which the stage actors drew their inspiration, I noted my 'impressions.' They were favorable, and if I'm guilty of nothing worse than failing to note the faults of those chosen by themselves as ringmasters of the performance, I feel that the Zelanians will not regret my having 'discovered them.'

"As the beauties of Zelania so far transcend the powers of the painter's brush and the poet's metaphor, I pay her homage of my admiration, in modest speech."

IN SILENT WONDER.

"In scenic wonders, these playful Isles present a peculiar series of thrilling charms, which seem to satisfy best the yearnings of those who have visited other lands.

"In geography, Zelania is beautifully isolated, as every beach is washed by more than a thousand miles of sea. Its borders are so erratic, so indented by bays, harbors, and inlets, that its shore-lines are over 4,000 miles in extent, and, in altitude, it reaches from the sea-shore to the clouds.

"Configuratively, it is milder than a dream, and topographically, it presents a most romantic and pleasing aspect. In scenic beauty, the Isles of Greece, the Lakes of Ireland, or the 'Vales of Cashmere' do not surpass it, and in the awe-inspiring wildness of its mountain grandeur, it rivals the noblest of Norway or Alaskan scenes.

"In bold magnificence, the glacial glories of the Swiss Alps are tame comparisons, and its geysers, its boiling lakes, its roaring vents from subterranean fires, its hundreds of spouting caldrons, its grottos and waterfalls, could not be surpassed, if all the rest of Oliffa's wonders were brought together and placed on exhibition—such a congerie of curiosities has Nature thrown in young Zelania's lap.

"When Nature made Oliffa, my children, she nourished a sly intent to show her skill when in the flower of training. With this in view, as she deftly moulded other lands and tempered them from her laboratory, she tossed aside the choice bits of material, and took notes on 'effect.' Then, after finishing the rest, and 'behold it was very good,' with a glance to the gallery gods, she said, 'Now look at me!'

Waimangu Geyser.—Semiquiescent.

"Then, like the sculptor who has many models for one figure—one from which to copy

the most perfect arm, one the hand, another the knee, and still another for the foot—so, she, selecting from the most perfect of all her former works, improved on each, and in her happiest mood she fashioned Zelania, and anchored it in these southern seas. Then she smiled, and—took a *siesta*."

Waimangu Geyser playing to a height of 1500ft. The second wonder of the world.

"Geologically," said Oseba, "Zelania is an ancient pile of dirt, but here all the games that frisky Nature played in her boisterous youth, before 'Atlantus' sank from the Ocean bosom, before the Mediterranean burst through the Pillars of Hercules, before the sun and winds drank the waters from the Sahara, and possibly before great Chimborazo was, she still keeps on the stage for the edification or the terror of gods and men."

"At Rotorua, that trysting place of fairies and fiends, man may play with Nature as did the deities of old with the daughters of men; while at Waimangu, the mightiest geyser on the globe, one may safely stand within a few yards' distance and behold a scene of thrilling awe that banishes all consciousness—save that of dread and power.

"To stand near the verge and behold this acre of dark world as it is hurled a thousand feet into the air, is worth a trip round this little globe. Language gives but a faint gleam of human passion, and every effort to describe this scene brings but a pathetic consciousness of human frailty. Beholding this mighty convulsion, even the thoughtless stand motionless and mute, and as Milton is dead, Waimangu will never be described in words.

"The countless mountain lakes, the wild fiords—from whose deep recesses one but rarely sees the sun—the shady solitudes, so painfully still that one shudders with a chilling sense of loneliness, and the easily-approached glaciers and waterfalls—many with a plunge of over a thousand feet, that amaze the Alpine traveller—thrill and fill the beholder with astonishment.

"But for one who enjoys the gun and the rod, there are such tempting opportunities for the diversion of the attention, that the imagination finds ready relaxation, and thus the body and mind gain vigor as the scenes and the days pass by.

"Then, Zelania's wonders may be visited with ease, comfort, and perfect safety. Her furies are on their good behaviour, and save on the borders of her terrors, her aspects are as serene as heaven's azure sky. Her mountains are rarely disturbed by the ravings of Pluto, her great geysers are forcible, but not dangerously erratic, and her boiling springs are so amiable that they may be studied and safely observed at short range.

"Zelania, thou art by far the most beauteous land,
E'er dreamed of fate, or reared by Nature's cunning hand.
You've heaven-piercing peaks, crowned with eternal snow,
A thousand boiling caldrons—heated from below.
You've glaciers dwarfing Alpine scenes, and fiords more wild
Than Norway boasts. When fashioned, God beheld and smiled.

"That Nature rather recklessly managed this country in early geological times is abundantly evident, but save the activity of the geysers and boiling lakes—which play for the amusement of visitors—and the occasional listing when some great personage steps too close to the edge, *terra* has been satisfactorily *firma* ever since the present managers were commissioned in the early '90's.

"In every natural feature, this is a country of boundless variety. In climate, it varies from Finland to Italy; and in production, by intelligent transplanting, most of the necessities of civilised life are here."

Here the notes say the poetess Vauline inquired whether Mr. Oseba had not minutely described some of these marvellous scenes in his report. With reverential mien, the sage replied:—

"No, my children, to attempt this, were to profane the gift and the giver of speech. Only one who beholds these wonders can appreciate them. When confronted, the grandeur of the infinite may be felt by a sensitive soul, but through an interpreter all attempts fail. Beholding one scene, I uncovered and bowed my head in silence.[A] Words! they were meaningless."

Yes, and I will help Mr. Oseba out, for I have observed these things, and I have read somewhere how some sort "rush in" where even the angels incline to hesitate.

The Painter came!

Folding his arms, he raised his drooping head, and gazed in awful thought.
He stood in rapturous dream; "Oh God, if I could grasp that scene, the noblest fame e'er bought
By toil were mine!" With eager hand he clutched the brush. With anxious eye
He gazed. Lo! the eye dimmed, the brain reeled, the hand fell, and with a sigh
He dropped the brush. In deep despair he turned and said, "Alas, good-bye!
'Tis an unpainted picture. Ye gods of solitude, good-bye!"

The Poet came!

With streaming hair, pale brow, and nervous tread he hither came to brood
O'er Nature's vastest works, to wrench the beauties from this solitude,
And weave in mystic rhyme these wond'rous scenes for common mortals' gaze.
Entranced, he seized his pen. Anon he wrote—methinks he wrote in praise.
Then pensively he stood, and mutt'ring said: "Words suit well the minstrel's lays,
But, 'tis an unwritten poem, to tempt the soul through endless days."

The Fool came!

He smiled. On good terms with himself he seemed, as one who owned the world.
In jocund speech he cried, "'Tis ours!" and in mock haste his flag unfurled.
On ancient log he rests. He laughs, he jokes, and chats. Behold him look!
'Tis for a match; he faggots brings, he lights a fire—a meal to cook.
Says he: "Extr'ordinary! Ar'nt this grand? By gol! old fel, I'll write a book."
Then words like snow-flakes fall—like snow-flakes in a brook.

A DIGRESSION.

"Now, my children," said Oseba, "permit me to make a few observations based upon my study among the Outeroos, which will apply to the country under review.

"Remember, all terms expressing quality—such as good and evil, right and wrong, truth and error—are relative, and, as affecting men, the definition to each individual depends upon his environment. As a fact, the rules expressing these ideas are largely fictions established by society for its own purpose, but, in their general application, they must be allowed considerable latitude.

"A country is good or bad, as it offers or withholds opportunity for earning a livelihood, and for the development of the mental faculties by the application of reasonable efforts; and a government is good or bad, as it withholds or encourages such opportunities and aspirations. 'When the wise rule, the people rejoice'—even in the barren districts. It is a matter—well, it is a matter—largely of 'grey matter.' As a rule, Nature has not been niggard in the distribution of her blessings. And, as a rule, the term good or bad, when applied to a country, applies less to the soil than to the society. It is college *versus* cannon, or inquiry *versus* credulity. Under a reign of benign justice, from a barren soil may arise an earthly paradise, while bigotry, war, and oppression will make a hell of the fairest valley.

'The gods wondered, and Viehnu said to Bel,
"With seven wise men shalt thou enter hell,
Or with five fools, pass into paradise."
"Give me," said Bel, "hell with the wise,
For that is heaven, where they do dwell,
While fools would make of Heaven itself a hell."'

"The subject, my children, always bears the image of the law, the expression of custom, and customs are established by cunning for the rule of credulity. By custom, one is born the owner of many broad acres; and by custom, ten thousand toil without enjoying, that one may enjoy without toil. But Nature usually lends herself freely to man's designs. In a vast monotonous country, despotism is a usual system of government, Nature suggesting no change; the leader becomes the chief, the chief becomes the monarch, the monarch becomes a despot, and the despot a god.

"On the contrary, in a smaller country with diversified aspects, indented shore-lines and water-front, scaleable mountains and erratic climate, Nature suggests—change. A holy discontent appears, the despot becomes a constitutional monarch, a parliament serves the people, a cabinet advises the king; and then, as mountains suggest liberty and seas adventure, distant colonies, in which custom and precedent are ignored, are established on lines in harmony with environing conditions.

"Human liberty, my children, rarely gains a victory in an old, wealthy, populous and well-established country or government. Society, under such conditions, becomes conservative; the rulers love power, the cunning want no change, the wealthy are satisfied, and the people, being adjusted to the changeless conditions, are 'loyal' and contented.

"Further, every defeat of despotism, every entrenchment upon the 'divine' territory, every victory of human liberty, has been due to the restless inhabitants of the water-front; and remember, for all the progressive movements of all the ages, and for what the centuries call modern civilisation, the world is indebted to colonial enterprise, conspicuously led by Phœnicia, Greece, and modern Britain."

BACK TO ZELANIA.

"But let us, my children," Oseba continued, "return to Zelania, Nature's choicest, last, and most successful effort, and to where these principles apply. In her geographical situation, her configuration, her soil and climate, she offers man everything to toughen the fibre, to quicken the perception, and to strengthen the imagination.

"She has the climate, the fertility, the production, the picturesqueness of Greece, and all in greater variety."

Oseba here led his audience into a most interesting inquiry regarding climatic influence in the development of a people. He said man was a part of, and strongly allied to, Nature, and that he could not escape the influence of his environment.

In interior tropical regions Nature puts a black skin and black hair on her people, and, as a joke, she usually flattens the nose. In vast interior and warm regions, the complexion are tawny, with black or tawny hair and oblique eyes, that shunt the direct rays of light.

"Then, too," he says, "island or sea-shore people are lighter in color than those of the interior, and not only is the complexion of man, but his physical proportions, stature and temperament, modified by climatic conditions. In interior countries men gradually assume a type—they are lithe, and rather small of stature, and so alike that they seem cast in the same mould; while those living on islands along the water-front, or among the mountains, are more sturdy, they vary more in build, size and deftness, and they are mentally more inquisitive, venturesome, impetuous and brave."

He said that by far the most sturdy, virile, impulsive and enterprising people on Oliffa inhabited the British Isles. Of course, the race had much to do with modern movements, but the earlier climatic conditions of the country produced the racial distinctions.

The Moa of Maoriland. The skeleton of this particular Moa stands about 12ft. high, and is a curious but substantial fact, but as the Moa, the dinornis—as the learned folks call it—permanently retired from New Zealand, possibly before the Maoris came, the plumage and plumpness are the works of the artistic naturalist.

"By the rule of Nature, then," he continued, "Zelania, with the proper stock to begin with, in complexion, form, feature, temperament, and mental endowments, should produce the finest type of man and womanhood on the planet."

He compared the Maoris with the aboriginals of interior Australia, and said both were modified by their environment.

Here Leo Bergin remarked that Mr. Oseba was certainly greatly taken and impressed by his "colonial" experience. However, it is not improbable that while travelling in New Zealand Mr. Oseba received sufficient courtesies to impress him deeply with the matchless hospitality of the people.

"But, enough," says Leo Bergin, "my master is worthy of my whole attention," and the notes run:—

"But let me return, my children, and pick up the theme of Zelania, for in her—with my tours over her romantic islands—I found balm for all my earlier disappointments.

"Zelania has certainly not worried her soul in life-producing efforts. In botany, she is not rich in species; in mammals she is more allied to South America, over six thousand miles distant, than to Australia, but twelve hundred miles, justifying my conviction that this paragon of beauty was an after-thought of the creative power.

"In mammals she has but a little rat—a poor little weakling that has not yet been tamed or learned to board with the people—and two little half-developed bats. Of reptiles, there are a few lazy lizards, but whether some 'Patrick' or 'Denis' had banished them, I could not say; but snakes, there are none."

He said there were some land birds, but as there were no animals to "make them afraid," the more indolent of them had lost their wings and their natural characteristics had changed.

The moa was probably—some time ago—a pretty respectable bird, but there being no danger from which to "flee" and no long flights to procure food, it cast off its wings and strutted about until its bones became as heavy as those of a reindeer, and it stretched up its head until it stood twelve feet high. But having no cares nor anxieties, no fears nor ambition, it failed to develop "grey matter," so when the Maori came it "surrendered," and, having taken off its flesh as well as its wings, it is now resting in the museums. Without the rod or the bun, there seems to be no effort, and without effort there seems to be little progress with any created thing.

THE MAORIS "DISCOVERED."

"And the great god Morduch heaved the earth from its watery bed, and peopled its shores according to his will."

As Oseba evidently meant to proceed upon his discourse in some predesigned order, he here gave some interesting attention to the Maoris, the natives—or, so-called, aboriginals—of New Zealand.

The orator, in his inimitable manner, described the Maoris with amusing detail. He calls them a fine race of romantic savages, whose physique had undoubtedly been greatly improved by the winning smiles of Zelania's climate and general aspects; for 'tis said they have been loafing around there for 500 years. "A large, heavy, dark brown people are these Maoris, who, in their own picturesque costume, often looked gracefully noble. Brave and ferocious while untamed, they are usually amiable and indolent when subjected to civilising influences."

Many of the young women were very pretty, and the children were quick in wit and movement. He did not think that tattooing the under lips of the women had really improved their beauty. Many of the half-castes were very intelligent, and not a few had made excellent reputations, in politics and other "professions." Many of them, too, had a sublime gift of "gab," and this trait is shared—even by the men.

Intellectually the Maoris were, Oseba thought, superior to any other tamed savage; but, like other barbarians, when touched by civilisation, they learned and accepted the vices more readily than the virtues. This was noticeable in all civilising movements. Oseba remarked that it was often observed among the Outeroos when speaking of such people, that the "Christian vices" killed them.

"This," he says, "was natural, for while it takes time to teach the 'brethren' the real advantages to be derived from the practices of Christian virtue, the 'Christian vices' yield 'immediate returns.' 'Thou shalt not steal' to a savage produces a peculiarly disagreeable confusion of ideas, and the advantages are not readily apparent, but two drinks of whisky rarely failed to impress. This is a custom peculiar to 'Christian culture' that is 'taking.'

"To judge by the conspicuous exhibitions of artistic effort and the countless displays by the photo fiend in many of Zelania's towns, a stranger would conclude that the Maoris were the 'superior' and dominant race, though there are but a little over 43,000 in the whole country, mostly on the north or warmer island, and it is said they are about stationary in numbers and in morals."

He told his audience that these Maoris, when originally discovered, were a stalwart, brave and rather superior race of savages; that war was the only argument that appealed to their perverted consciences, and he quoted an admiring New Zealand poet to prove the "amiable" heroism of the Maori "ladies."

"E'en woman, formed for sweetness, for love, and tender art
Here showed the tiger instinct, the hard and ruthless heart;
Her's was the task in battle, the wounded braves to slay,
And cook the reeking corpses for the feast that closed the fray."

"Yes, the Maori women were brave, very brave, but, my children, in all Zelania there was not a mouse.

"Of these Maoris, there are several tribes," he says, "who, when free from the meddlesome 'white man's yoke,' are usually engaged in slaying and stewing each other, and, besides carving with their greenstone cleavers their cooked brethren and their own faces, they practised much in wood-carving. In this, while the workmanship is fair, there is a manifest lack of a sense of proportion, that amuses the connoisseur as it delighted the amateur in art.

"Like the more common, or at least more numerous and more pretentious white fellow-citizen, these Maoris go to church some, and to school, and to the drink-shop and to jail, but as the Maoris have a little creed of their own, they don't go to church very much. But if the Maori goes less to church, to school, and to Parliament, he also goes less to jail and to the hotel than his more pretentious white British fellow-citizen.

"The Maoris are picturesque, especially at the more popular tourist resorts, where their presence lends a particularly charming romance to the occasion. The emotional tourist—especially if a young gentleman from 'Home'—who is safely piloted by the alert, polite, and loquacious 'Maggie' among the roaring and exploding geysers of that charming compromise between awe-inspiring beauty and terror, that unpreached sermon, that unsung song, that unwritten poem, that section of hell in an earthly paradise, Rotorua, in whose weird precincts are seen and heard and smelled, at close range, the seething fires of 'Pluto's dread abode,' he will cherish a generous respect for Maori hospitality forever. Under Maggie's watchful guidance, the most unsophisticated tourist could safely approach the yawning mouth of these boiling caldrons without endangering life or health or appetite; though, unless one heeds the cautious guide, the boot soles are in danger of shrinking, and in these sulphurous regions 'kuss words' flow from pious lips.

"Nature," Oseba argued, "was a unity and is consistent. She ignores individuals, and strives, oblivious to time, for universals. No created thing ever escapes the influence of environment. But Nature carries out her works with the instruments at hand. Whence came these Maoris is a guess, but as in character, stature, proportion, personal bearing, and mental possibilities, no other savage on the globe compares with them, they must have been sufficiently long in Zelania to have become modified by, and made to conform to, the luring conditions of that wonderful country."

But I must continue:—

As there were no indigenous grains or tameable animals, and as no people ever worked out a civilisation without the assistance of tameable animals, the Maori could only remain a savage, but the climate and general aspect of Nature, the peculiar environing conditions, gave him the noblest soul and most fertile intellect ever housed in the brain of a barbarian. The conduct of the Maoris in defence of their country, considering the relative conditions of the contending forces, found no parallel in history or romance.

They had all the cunning and duplicity of the Greek, the stubborn courage of the ancient Briton, and the stoical disdain for death of the North American Indian. While in the whirligig of the great world's doings a contest between the most skilful of all warriors and a few small tribes of savages, in so remote a country, could excite no very great interest among the far-away nations, to the watchful student of events there were few pages of history more interesting than the Maori wars in Zelania.

Socially, the Maori was of a peculiar mould. A communist in property, he was an aristocrat by nature, and in his soul there was a haughty exuberance of spirit that rendered tribal discipline difficult, and domestic peace precarious. In war, the Maori was brave; in diplomacy, shrewd; in council, a born orator.

The Maori remained a savage in Zelania because there was nothing to tame him, but in his nature there was the diamond, and, by a little grinding, its brilliancy always burst forth. His native environment had given him everything of a superior mould but the final touch. I quote:—

"Already from the grim huts of these late savages have come forth the orator, the lawyer, the statesman, and the successful business man. 'From the cannibal feast to the Cabinet,' is almost true of the Maori.

"The fate of the Maoris?

"Well, my children, I don't know, but the grafting of civilisation on such a stock may work wonders, and to study these most picturesque of all the sons of Nature, is worth a journey around this little world.

Tattooed Maori Chief.— "Maori Carving."

"It is most interesting," continued Oseba, "to study the aboriginals of any country, and it is pathetic to observe their gradual retirement from the earth's fair face; but the Maori—the handsome, haughty, aristocratic and eloquent Maori—is as different from all other uncivilised races as his enchanting island home is different from all other countries on the surface of Oliffa.

"If bare-handed Nature in Zelania, with no animals for the chase, none for herds or for servants of industry, and practically no grain or fruit, could spank the savage, common to other lands into this shape, what may it not do for civilised man, who brings with him all the aids of all the ages?"

Oseba explained that before he called on Zelania he had visited every other country on Oliffa, and had studied the "inferior" races carefully, but the Maoris stood solitary and alone. All others lacked physical fibre and mental stamina, and for them to remain in contact with the superior races meant many generations for doubtful growth, or a few generations for extinction.

But the Maoris had now attained full manhood. They were "different" from the whites, and this was more proper than to say they were very much "inferior." They had enjoyed none of the advantages of outside communication, no aid from tameable animals, no experiences by the chase, no traditions of industrial art, during probably more than five hundred years. Yet the Maori seems to have attained to a surprising degree a fairly full mental and physical stature. He has eloquence, perception, inquisitiveness and acquisitiveness. He has everything but—civilisation. He has the soul, but it needs tuning; the material, but it needs shaking-up and seasoning. The magic touch of a newer, a higher inspiration is needed, and that is being injected into his awakening consciousness by a benign social sentiment.

"To-day," said Oseba, "the Zelania Maori, as seen in his grotesque works of art, in his struggle for wild independence, in his weird religious ceremony, in his common avocations as toiler, professional man or politician, is the most picturesque human being on the planet, and his presence in Zelania gives a seasoning of romance to be studied and enjoyed in no other land."

SCENE VIII.—Act II.

APPROPRIATING A WORLD.

ALL being in readiness, a number of very perfect maps were thrown on the canvas, showing the plains, valleys, mountains, lakes, and rivers of Zelania, with the nature of the production of each island; and a careful and detailed description as to location and resources was given by the orator.

Then, calling the attention of his audience, Oseba notified the people that he was now reaching the closing chapter of his report, or in our refined phrase he was on "the home stretch." He said:—

"Now, my children, at this stage of our inquiry, I desire to remind you again how closely man is allied to Nature; how he is adjusted to all the environing conditions; how the fresh breezes of a temperate zone give him a fair skin; how a varied and pleasing aspect gives him a cheerful temperament; how the mountains suggest to him freedom, and the seas adventure; how climate depresses or exhilarates; how pastoral pursuits awaken the romantic in his nature; agriculture, patience and sturdy industry; and the search for precious metals, a careless independence and intelligence.

"Then, for this last, let the Titans wrest from Nature all that conspired to make the Phœnician, the Greek, the Norse, and the Briton, and mould them artistically into the most pleasing form, and lo! Zelania would appear in her pristine glory to—fashion a man."

Here he briefly described the workings of the government of Zelania, how it had adopted the parliamentary system of Britain, and that, while it acknowledged a proud allegiance to the British crown, it was probably the most unmitigated democracy the world had ever beheld.

"As a member of a compact," Oseba said, "Zelania owes but a loose allegiance to the Motherland, for she is at liberty to part the cable at any time and float away with the parental blessings. But, as a fact, she is held by a sentiment stronger than bands of steel; and by the voluntary sacrifice of many of her noblest sons on distant fields, she has proven, not only her loyalty to the Crown, but her love for the Empire and her devotion to British aspiration. Theirs is not merely the loyalty of the subject—'tis the tender regard of children for the generous kindred of homeland.

"Now, my children," continued the orator, "I am going to show you another series of views, some the works of man, and some the works of Nature, that have influenced my actions. Glance through the album I have given you, and you will see the style of men, who, on the lines so strongly suggested by the inviting environment, have fashioned the social creeds of the country.

"It is a grand thing to behold men strong enough and brave enough to lead the people up, not to where they may 'see the promised land,' but to secure for them and their children a nobler heritage than Joshua ever saw or Moses ever dreamed of."

The orator claimed that though the mightiest imagination could not reach a comprehension of these enchanting scenes, he felt that the views presented would justify his claim that of all lands Zelania was the most wonderful on the globe.

And now he proceeded to call attention to the human side—how the denizens of this most favored country were using their peerless opportunities, and this was even more wonderful, for Nature followed rules and precedents, while these people broke them.

"A man may famish," said Oseba, "surrounded by the most dazzling splendor; he may starve, amid the most wild, weird and stupendous beauty; but when erratic Nature has strewn in the same garden that which most elevates the soul and administers most to the nourishment of the body, man should tender the tribute of his admiration and gratitude, and—'go to work.'"

In Zelania, as I interpret the orator's meaning, the gods have conspired to do all this, and to make the lot of man a happy one. But in a life so frail and so full of wants, the practical side deserves consideration, for while the Deity may furnish the paddock, he will not throw blood oranges on fern trees, or grow "A No. 1" cauliflower on ground not subdued by the spade or the plough.

After having made so fine an exhibition of the choice spots of Zelania, Oseba commented upon the peculiar notions of the Outeroos regarding their visits to other lands. He said by the Outeroos' measure, he himself had been the world's greatest "discoverer," for he had found and charted the whole outer surface. He had "discovered" China, Japan, Russia, and other countries; he had discovered Africa, America, Australia, and finally the "Paradise of Oliffa"—Zelania.

Many people on Oliffa did not care to be "discovered"—in fact, would rather not have been, and, among these, were not improbably, those fading Maoris of Zelania. The "discoverer" had been the bane of many a people— remember the color-line!

Oseba told his people that "Zelania was once discovered by Tasman in 1642, and that it was not discovered again for more than a hundred years, when Cook found it in 1769. Later, to the temporary joy and final regret of the

Maoris, the French also 'discovered' the country, and soon some gentlemen from Sydney called, and in 1814 the 'parsons' found it, since which time the collections have been regular. I," said he, "am Zelania's last 'discoverer,' and my report shall be a modest one.

"In 1840 the Union Jack was permanently nailed up in queenly Auckland, Zelania being made a province of New South Wales, and the next year the country was erected into a colony, with a good billet for the favorite of a British Premier.

"In 1865 the capital was removed to Wellington, a very breezy city, with fine 'sloping' hills at no great distance from the water-front.

"As in other British colonies, government here meant liberty, and, as in all habitable countries liberty means progress, Zelania has had a full measure of prosperity, practically from the beginning.

"If," proceeded Oseba, "the Outeroos ever evolve a generation of thinking men, the mystery of mysteries to them will be how a people as educated and business-like as the generation, who discovered and developed steam and electricity, and the modern commercial systems could be stupid enough to give away or sell to a few of the people the land upon—and from—which all the people must necessarily live. Further, it will be interesting to inquire by what course of reasoning the temporary custodians of the public domain arrived at a conclusion that they could rightfully alienate it, ignoring the will and the right of all who might come by the next train.

"As broad, as almost limitless, as is the meaning of supreme authority among the Outeroos, by no compromise with expediency, by no stretch of the imagination, can any human power consign the future generation to a madhouse, or to homelessness, or to a condition of serfdom under the heirs of the more fortunate few; but to grant the lands to a small number of persons is to pawn the cage in which the animals are eternally locked.

"Unfortunately, before the 'rulers' of Zelania had been broadened by the pure air of this wonderland, they had parcelled out much of the better lands to a comparatively few persons. But the grapes fed by the early rulers to the parents of the colonials, set the teeth of the children on edge.

"The area of Zelania is 104,000 square miles, as against 124,000 for the United Kingdom; and the population is 800,000, as against 40,000,000 for the United Kingdom.

"But, behold the growing wisdom of the generations! In the United Kingdom, by inheritance, by the crimes of authority, a few hundred families, or less than one out of every 2,000 of the population, 'own' nearly one-half of the whole country; while in this new world, the smaller follies of earlier rulers are already being corrected, and the lands are being rescued from baronial control and held for 'the people,' regardless of the time of the arrival of their train.

"As the Outeroos are mostly land animals, my children, and as we have learned how important the land is to human happiness, I will give you briefly this phase of the social situation of Zelania as being developed by its present leaders."

Then he reminded his audience that Zelania embraced 104,000 square miles or about 66,000,000 acres of land.

Mr. Oseba claimed that the British Isles, with 79,000,000 acres, with a considerable area of waste, support nearly 40,000,000 people; Italy with about 70,000,000 acres, with much waste, supports 30,000,000 people; Prussia, with about 90,000,000 acres, large areas of waste, supports 31,000,000 people; France, with about 125,000,000 acres, with extensive mountain regions, supports nearly 40,000,000 people; and that Belgium and Holland, with about 18,000,000 acres, and much waste, support over 10,000,000 people.

He argued that if the estimates were approximately correct, this most favored of all lands on the surface of Oliffa would support, on a like plane of living of the Italians, 22,000,000 of people; on a like plane of the French, 12,000,000 people; and on a like plane of the British Isles, at least 10,000,000 of people.

But he explained that with a like population of these countries a like plane of living would be inevitable; so, for the happiness of Zelania, he thought, it was fortunate that many splendid obstacles stood in the way of a rapid increase in population. The cry for population was the most delusive mockery that ever lured a people to the verge of misery.

Here I quote the intrepid discoverer:—

"B-i-g does not spell 'great.' China has what most of the new countries of Oliffa are screaming for—'population.' Yet China is not considered 'great.' India, even with British rule, as a people or a race is not 'great.' The true greatness of a nation consists in the greatness of the individual units composing the nation, and not in their numbers. America is great as a nation, but the real average 'greatness' of the individual American has been declining for many years. Better travel comfortably with a select party than rush to ruin in a crowded train.

"There is no relation between size and value. Even the most ambitious Outeroo would hardly claim Lambert, who weighed forty stone, to have been 'greater' than little Pope, who looked like an interrogation point and weighed but eight. So, as there is no virtue in avoirdupois, there is no 'greatness' in mere numbers. Better flirt with one healthy girl, than take a dozen sour old maids to the pantomime."

Mr. Oseba might have mentioned, had he known the facts, that Phœnicia, that gave to the world the ship and the alphabet, and anticipated modern commercial methods, occupied but a small strip of country—mostly sterile—from eight to twenty-five miles wide, and less than a hundred and eighty miles long; that Attica, at the feet of whose philosophers we still sit, from whose artists we still copy, and to whose orators we still listen, embraced but seven hundred square miles; and that the population of Sparta, while in her glory, probably never exceeded ten thousand souls.

"No, my children," said Oseba, "b-i-g, does not spell 'great,' and any Zelanian who is caught howling for 'population' should be compelled to 'shout' for the whole crowd until he goes 'broke,' and has to hunt a billet to enable him to buy a beer and a bun. The desirable cannot be bribed—others should not be wanted."

THE MAORI MAID OF ROTORUA.

Did you ever see Maggie of Rotoru'?
You would never imagine what she can do

For the mouths of hell,
With a magic spell,
This little brown maid—
As I have said—
Will lead you over, and under and through.

This little brown damsel of Rotoru'
Will laugh at the fates, and smile at you.
Like a fairy dream,
Through the caldron's steam,
In gleeful wit.
She'll gaily flit—
Yet careful, stranger, how you pursue.

With this little brown maid of Rotoru'
You scramble and gaze and wonder, too.
You stand appalled,
Your soul's enthralled,
For scenes so weird,
Have here appeared—
You wonder if h—— isn't bursting through.

While much of this danger, my friends, is sham
God tempers the winds to the little shorn lamb.
But wild Nature raves
In dark hidden caves,
And 'tis romance, you know,
To Roto' you go,
So leave some "memory" in Maggie's palm.

Here, Leo Bergin, with a deep love for Zelania, "pimples out into poetry"—
"on his own," as follows:—

ZELANIA'S GREETING.

Zelania's stores are rich in wine,
Zelania's air is sweet with flowers,
Zelania's sons are rich in kine,
Zelania's maidens wile the hours,
'Mid scenes of matchless beauty.
Zelania's valleys waive with grain,
Zelania's hills are white with sheep,
Zelania's sons are skilled in gain,
Zelania's maidens ever keep
The path that leads to duty.

Zelania's crown is rich and rare,
Zelania's laws are wise and free,
Zelania's sons and daughters care,
Zelania's door to ever see
Swung open wide, and then—
Zelania speaks across the seas,
Zelania calls in welcome voice,
Zelania sends by every breeze
Zelania's greeting to the choice—
Of earth's deserving men.

Well, that is as refreshing as it is novel. Mr. Oseba and Leo are both right, and I say, "Well done!" for a popular gentleman of old said: "He that provideth not for his own household has denied the faith, and is worse than an infidel," and if this was Paul, he was not far "beside" himself on this occasion.

It is very pleasing mental recreation to talk about the "brotherhood of man" and the equal rights of "all the children of God" to play anywhere on the surface of His "footstool," but Nature suggests that "every living creature" shall hold down its claim or it will be crowded out, and this same cruel, relentless, unsympathising "Nature"—that always "barracks" for her longest-clawed children—helps to shovel the weak into the compost heap.

With the achievements of modern times, with industrial progress, specialised effort and rapid transit, the many-hued people of the earth may enjoy the fruits of all lands without practising at the same bar or sitting at the same table.

That "God made all men equal" is pretty—it is very pretty; but it lacks the merit of scientific truth, and while it may be desirable—profitable—to deal with the outside "barbarian," and to aid, educate, and elevate him, none but a fool or a fanatic would bring a hoard of park loafers into his dining-room and seat them at his table, to the exclusion of his own children—or his wife's relations.

We may do justice by a "brother" man without boarding him or converting him into a brother-in-law.

Mr. Oseba said:—

"Zelania's needed population will arrive in due season, for, besides her own resistless attractions, Oliffa must be more densely covered; but in 'filling up the country' from abroad, the heads should be weighed and not counted. Zelania may select her own coming population, for whether for health, for profit, for pleasure, for curiosity, or to study lessons of the highest social and political wisdom, she is curiosity's magnetic pole, and with prudent management on the part of her 'rulers' she will soon become the happy loitering place for the leisure-loving, wealthy, and well-to-do of all lands. Then, thousands of those who 'call' will be so charmed with her faultless climate, her romantic scenery, her hospitable people, and her splendid opportunities for domestic happiness and private gain, that they will cast their lots in this ever-enchanting land.

"Nature points to Zelania and says to all her children:—

"'Come and see what I did when I had my hand in.' Then, my children, let me anticipate, for I desire that you may now have a glimpse of the goal to which I am leading you.

"Well, I may tell you these British people to whom I have briefly referred, composed almost exclusively in this case of English, Irish and Scotch, being far removed from central authority, so strongly tempted by new opportunities, and so resistlessly influenced by new and pressing demands, have amazed the world by the boldness of their political conceptions and by their marvellous achievements in social experiments."

From Mr. Oseba's oration one would conclude that never did a colony of loyal people more readily depart from traditional usages, never did a community enter into the possession of a new country who so readily adjusted themselves by their customs, their laws, and their rules of action to the requirements of a novel environment as did the settlers of this peerless land.

He claimed that, in little more than half a century, before they were three-quarters of a million souls, by their achievements in social evolution the Zelanians had excited the interest and won the admiration of the civilised world.

"Selfishness," he argued, "is the mainspring of human action, and the actuating motive of every human being is to secure the greatest possible happiness with the least possible expenditure of physical toil.

"Though the social instincts of man help to tame him, all social and political systems in the world are based upon very human traits. The savage, for his own happiness, by force appropriates whatever he wants or can get. The half-civilised man cunningly appropriates the land, that its fruit may ripen in his granary, that himself and family may be happy, while the really civilised man would divide the opportunities among all, and his happiness is found in the general joy. The Zelanians are being civilised by evolution and parliamentary enactments.

"And they allotted the land as each had need."

Oseba reaffirmed his conclusions that no people ever took possession of a new country who shaped the land laws with a due regard to those who came later—with rights just as holy—save the Zelanians. In this they were more nearly complying with the rational demands of justice than any other people.

"I will give you," said he, "a glimpse of the policy now in vogue, and how it seems to satisfy the hopes of its sponsors, for this will deeply interest you."

The orator here began a review of the land system of Zelania, and, with a view to brevity, the notes will be "boiled down" to the lowest possible comprehensive space.

As the country was originally divided into some nine provinces with as many governing bodies, each vested with authority to deal with and dispose of the public domain, there naturally arose a system that resulted in great inequality, as well as in great confusion. Then as all the provinces were in need of roads, bridges, schools, and other public improvements, they vied with each other in offering inducements for immigration or new population, and with a hand exceedingly lavish, the lands were alienated—often in large tracts.

When the Colonial Parliament took over the public property—by an abolition of provincial authority—the land question at once assumed a new importance. This came about at the most intense stage of the modern transitionary period. "Industrial progress" had ushered in the most resistless spirit of commercial expansion in all countries. Then population became a "necessity" and railway construction became almost a mania everywhere.

The contagion struck Zelania. Public improvements were an absolute necessity, and the lands were the chief assets and "capital." For a time the lands were recklessly sold, but the mania for internal improvements became so unconquerable that foreign capital was called, and by a resort to the seemingly most reckless borrowing policy ever indulged in by a sane people, the lands were partially saved for a better future.

I quote:—

"Of the 66,000,000 acres there are said to be 35,500,000 'occupied,' and of this, 16,000,000 acres are 'freehold,' 11,000,000 are held under various crown leases, while the rest is leased from private owners, or from the natives—who own, as a people, several million acres. As the Maoris are usually tired, these lands are mostly leased to the 'superior race,' who do the work.

"The number of holdings is 115,713, with an improved value of £120,981,599. This is good. It shows an unparalleled proportion of land-holders, but it is not enough, and the 'Government' is making strenuous efforts to increase proportionately the population of rural districts, and of 'land holders,' if not of land 'owners.'

"Under an old system, the lands were so recklessly disposed of that even yet fully one-fourth of those 'occupied' are 'owned' by comparatively few people; but the Government has applied a strong 'persuader'—graduated land tax—and the great inequality will gradually disappear. The issue now is, 'custom *versus* justice,' and with the face turned to the new, the old loses its potency. The burden should be more on the land and less on the laundry.

"The laws and rules applied to the land of Zelania of late years, not only take into consideration the desires and requirements of would-be occupiers, but also the class of the land—the holdings for the better to be smaller in area than those for the poorer tracts. Of good or first-class land, under certain tenures, 640 acres only may be taken or held, and of second-class, 2,000 acres.

"There are several tenures under which 'crown lands' in Zelania may be acquired—one by purchase for cash; one with lease and right to purchase, rent to be 5 per cent. on unimproved value; and one, an eternal lease (999 years) with a rent of 4 per cent. during this period on original capital value—unimproved. Compulsory residence of the holder is enjoined during the currency of the lease in leasehold tenures.

"Under the *ægis* of the law, if wise and just, people are encouraged and assisted by the Government in forming small agricultural communities of not less than twelve heads of families—for the Outeroos have families—and this group may have set apart for them a suitable block of land upon which to settle. This secures educational advantages, for in every community the Government not only establishes schools, but compels parents to send their children for instruction.

"But when conscience was thoroughly aroused, it became evident to the most casual observer, that the great estates not only stood in the way of social progress, but that holding vast areas out of cultivation was a menace to the future liberties of the people. And further, that though there were considerable Crown lands suitable for occupation, the conditions for 'closer settlement' on them were not over favorable; and, further still, that every successful effort to settle these lands not only vastly increased the value of the great estates, but increased the temptation of the large owner to further extend his domain.

"Under the earlier *régime* the follies of the old rapidly spread over the new world, and by 1890 most of the better lands in Zelania were parcelled out in lordly estates and owned by a few persons.

"Almost before the people were aware of the tendencies of the times, a gigantic land monopoly threatened to overshadow the country. But being 14,000 miles from central authority, the affections of the people for hoary customs had weakened, and vested rights in ancient wrongs soon began to find earnest protestation.

"The rights of imminent domain were understood, the people had no notion of erecting a landed aristocracy, and a few bold souls, who, by the force of inherent genius had arisen from the industrial ranks, conceived the idea of writing another chapter in the history of human progress.

A Maori Beauty.

"No people," Mr. Oseba argued, "ever yet revolted against a despot who ruled with smiling diplomacy, but having learned in the old home the power of the world owners, and knowing that the liberties of none are secure where a few are vested with the instruments of oppression, people in this new and strange country felt the weight of the lordly hand possibly before it was ungloved for action.

"The land barons, with their sheep, inhabited the fertile valleys, while the people with their children, roamed over the sterile hills. But with the squeezing of the people into the bush there was a rush of brains to the head, and the chosen guardians of the public weal said: 'Zaccheus, come down.'

"Though New Zealand mutton was of good quality and wool bore a good price, some healthy gentlemen concluded that men and women and children were about as good as sheep, especially when the sheep belonged to the other fellow, and as the barons had no blunderbusses and the people had votes, the world-owners were called down to pay a little more of the taxes, and the people were called up to earn a square meal.

"Then the show was opened—without a prayer or a corkscrew—and some very sensible men who stood on firm ground suggested that any man who had muscle and a mouth should have an opportunity to exercise the one for the satisfaction of the other, and when the world-owners declined to 'set a price,' the agents of this brave democracy came with a persuader, and the revolution was begun.[B]

"The land barons were treated honorably. The values created by the coming of a progressive population, by the settlement on Crown lands, and by the construction of the highways, were generously allowed them; but when asked to move off the grass and make room for closer settlement, they learned to accept the situation, and the laws had a soothing influence.

"The graduated land tax is a powerful persuader, and already there have been about seventy of the great estates resumed and divided into small allotments among an intelligent, industrious and progressive people. And still the work goes on with success, and even profit in nearly every case.

"In Zelania has been demonstrated, not only the possibility but the wisdom of State landlordism. To-day the State is a landlord to the extent of over 15,000,000 acres, it has 16,000 tenants, and in all these resumptions, divisions, settlements, rent collections and management, there has been no loss, few grievances and fewer scandals.

"Then, too, when the estates are cut up and divided among settlers, schools are established, post offices are opened, roads are made, and—when needed by the settlers—money is loaned to them by the State at a reasonably low interest; and, so far, these laws have been to the infinite advantage of the people, and a profit to the State—the 'profits' used to further the general scheme.

"With this policy of graduated land tax and discretionary resumptions, exorbitant rents and land speculations are inconvenient, and with the 'loan to the settler policy' the money sharks can't squeeze the people, 'they can't.'

"In Zelania, the State, or the people in their organised capacity, aids from the general store the people in their individual capacity—to help themselves.

"The State gives nothing. There is humiliating charity nowhere, but elevating justice everywhere. The State puts a man on a farm, loans him money, helps him up hill, and then demands that he play the Hercules. It will loan him a spade—not to lean upon or to pawn, but to dig with—and he must keep it bright and pay for its use.

"The idea in Zelania, my children, is to have no lords and no paupers—that all men shall be producers, and not vagrants; tax-payers, and not tax-eaters—and that every citizen shall become a sturdy democrat, who will honorably strive as a stock-holder in a paying concern.

"Joint encouragement is given," said he, "and that may be called socialistic; but individual action is demanded, and that is democratic.

"Many persons in Zelania think that the government train is rushing ahead too rapidly, but these should observe the tendencies of the times, and realise the advantages of the general prosperity. Many others think the train moves too slowly, but these should realise the conservatism of wealth, the dangers of exploring uncharted seas, and they should remember that to-day, in all the essentials of human progress, they are by far the most advanced of all peoples.

"Of course, there are occasional failures in Zelania, enough to furnish healthy examples; for while any man who will hustle may thrive, the Almighty does not line up the jerseys for every lout that likes cream in his chocolate. Even in Zelania, the man who claims that this world owes him a living must make some effort to collect that little bill.

"As a fact, in Zelania they furnish a fellow with about everything but brains. This, doubtless, they would willingly do, but as there are a few things in which Nature seems to practice economy, so far there has appeared no surplus of brains—no, not even in Zelania."

Here I cluster some of Mr. Oseba's graphic conclusions into my own "chaste" language:—

Having become familiar with the serene security of the man of acres in other lands, it is curiously interesting to observe that people in Zelania—common and no account as they are in most countries—are held in considerable respect, regardless of their bank accounts, or the social position of their father-in-law.

In most countries, on Oliffa, the people are "moved on" to make room for animals, and, in most countries on Oliffa, the larger the "estate," the more easily can it be made larger; but in Zelania, when too many people are "out in the cold," some fellow with a big paddock is requested to "set a price," and the stray "sheep" are soon comfortably quartered and employed.

Under the old system such "estates" were always held "sacred," but in Zelania, among the most "sacred" of all recognised rights is the "sacred right" of "man to live"; and it has been discovered that to talk of the "sacred right" of a man to live, without an opportunity to earn something upon which to live, is an insult to God's noblest creatures; and the graduated land tax has so conciliated the lordly inheritors, that the "blessed" who "hunger and thirst" are not asked to wait for the platter of "charity," but they are "filled" from the products of their own strong hands.

Here I quote:—

"The Christian Outeroos, my children, all think they are in the world by the special desire and fiat of God, and yet of all the civilised Outeroos, the Zelanians alone have had courage enough to demand standing room on a world where God had placed them.

"They assume to think their deity made the world and then made them to people it, yet most of them have been persuaded that 'He made the world' for just a few of them, who are privileged to put up the notice 'Keep off the grass.' The Zelanians alone have removed the 'notice.'

"While to us, my children, so far away, with so long a history behind us, even these measures seem but the cautious experiments of amateurs, they are the most advanced known to the Outeroos; and the Zelanians, in their numerical 'fewness,' their national youth, and their splendid isolation, are more courageously grappling with the difficulties that have baffled the noblest statesmanship of all the ages, than any other social group in the world's progressive history.

"Zelania, my children, is the most unmitigated democracy ever known to the outer world of this planet, yet her people have just gained a glimpse, not a realisation, of human liberty. But the divine flame from the sacred torch is spreading, the public conscience is aroused, the public intellect is alert, and the social train is moving rapidly.

"What the dreamers, the poets, and the academicians of other lands laud as social ideals, the tradesmen, the farmers, and the mechanics of Zelania discuss as every-day matters of practical politics.

"'Touch not the Lord's anointed' hath saved the head of many a despot, and touching appeals for the observance of the 'sacred rights'—in hoary wrongs—hath larded the ribs of idleness for a very protracted season, but the Zelanians, in the exuberance of a novel situation, are indulging in mental gymnastics, and putting on grey matter—with results.

"A shipwrecked mariner, tossed on a lone island, rich with food, and shelter, and material for raiment, may 'own' that little world—for a time. His rights are supreme. He has a 'vested interest.' He 'discovered' it. As a contribution to the world's wealth he had practically created that patch of dirt. It is his. But suppose the next morning another fellow from the same or some other ship is tossed on the island. Well, number one must 'divvy.' The social conditions have changed. 'Right' has a new definition—unless the first enslaves the other.

"Definitions change. Right and wrong as expressing the various social theories, are fictions established by society for its own use, and if a rule established by society for the benefit of itself cannot be modified by society for the benefit of a larger social self, one man might own all the people who might be cast on the island—even if the island became a continent.

"The Zelanians have discovered that despotism consists chiefly in a loyal observance of ancient customs, and they are giving new definitions to old terms—and then adjusting society upon the new definitions. In no country are human rights more respected, or vested interests more sacredly guarded, than in Zelania, but the outposts are extended, and no longer is the power of the few to legally wrong the many, sanctified as a sacred right.

"In Zelania it has been decreed," said the sage Oseba, "that one man's rights must stop where another's begins—especially if there are several of the 'others.' In Zelania it has been decreed that the interests of 'all of us' are paramount to the interests of 'a few of us,' and, though the rights of no man must be infringed, the equal rights of the many must not be withheld.

"Man is a social being, and how much of his rights—as defined by himself— he may be called upon to yield for the happiness of many—as defined by themselves—has nowhere been determined.

"In Zelania, my children, the people have ideas, and the people rule. In Zelania the people may ask the lucky fellow who first struck the lonely island to 'set up a price.' They may ask that he who toils shall enjoy, that the size of a paddock be decreased, that the distance between drinks be increased, and, in Zelania, the statesmen with fidelity carry out the will of the people as expressed under the rules prescribed.

"Now, my children, I have dwelt with some detail on the land system of Zelania, for of all nations on the surface of Oliffa, the Zelanians are gradually adjusting themselves most wisely to the permanent happiness of the people—and we may desire to send thither a 'colony.'

"Zelania is a lovely land, my children, and, were there no principle involved, I would like to own it myself; but, alas! no 'principle' should be violated for so transient a pleasure."

Maori Woman and Child. Fashionably tattooed lip.

SCENE VIII—Act III.

UTILITARIAN.

HERE the notes record that there had been a half-hour's recess, during which Leo Bergin mentions that he enjoyed a pleasant chat with the poetess Vauline, that she was very charmingly inquisitive, and that while he confessed his lack of eloquence as compared with that of Oseba, he thought Zelania had lost nothing through his modesty.

Leo remarks that he showed the poetess many photos of the outer world, especially some fine ones of Zelania—among others, some of the leading statesmen and jurists—"all at the same sitting."

But I will ring off Leo Bergin, and have Amoora Oseba continue his observations, as per Leo's notes boiled down—by the fire of genius.

Mr. Oseba, on rising, is noted to have observed that men were human, to which I partially agree.

Taking from the immortal Robert as a text,

"Man's inhumanity to man
Makes countless thousands mourn,"

he delivered a long and eloquent oration on man's relations to this world; how the earth is the storehouse of Nature; how all that we call wealth, and the things that contribute to our health, comfort, and well-being are the products of the toil of men; and he then observed how few of us get much exercise out of this useful occupation.

As a fact, he conveyed the rather startling information that, as relating to actual production, fully nine-tenths of us were on vacation, or, to put a point on it, that every toiler was carrying about nine more easy-going souls on his back. These remarks applied to general productive industry.

Mr. Oseba explains "how in sparsely settled countries, where there are animals, primitive man lives by the chase, where there are tameable animals he becomes partially tamed and lives by his flocks, and where there is good soil—as population increased—the people turn to agriculture, and with more culture and more people industry becomes specialised, and commerce arises to put on the finishing touches.

"But," he argued, "as man clings to the muscles with which his ancestors flapped their ears, so he clings to all the habits practised by man in the past. He lives by the chase as long as there is room, he reduces nomadic industry to a science, and by co-operation all contribute to the advancement of the higher ideal.

"In Zelania, save for sport, the chase has been abandoned, and the living and wealth come from herding on, delving into, or cultivating the soil."

I gather from Leo's notes, that of some 66,000,000 acres of land in Zelania, there are but 6,000,000 subdued by the plough, 1,400,000 acres in crops, 4,600,000 acres in grass, and 7,000,000 unploughed—also in exotic grasses—and that chiefly from this source of wealth 800,000 of the best fed, best clothed, best housed, best educated and best satisfied, most progressive, healthy, happy and free people, that ever loafed about on the surface of this planet are quite alive, and satisfied to remain—*sine die.*

In grain and root crops, etc, the soil yields more abundantly than that of any other country. In pasture it carries more stock, in fruit it is promising, and as for the dairy, Denmark must fight to retain her laurels.

It will be seen that but a small portion of the land of Zelania is devoted to its "best use," so there is room for many millions of people, whose lot there should be blessed indeed, for in no country is the fortune of the land dweller so happy a one. His soil is fertile, his climate is genial, his seasons are reliable, his health is perfect, he has the best implements in use, his taxes are light, and his prices are always good. Happy Zelania's farmer!

SOME THAT ADAM NAMED.

"And God made the beasts of the earth after his kind, and cattle after their kind, and everything that creepeth upon the earth after his kind, and God saw that it was good."

But only a few miserable little "creeping things" got to Zelania, until the British brought others.

Oseba, in a review of the "animal business," remarked, that as all animals—save the long-wooled goat herded on the desert and mountain sides—had long retired from Cavitorus to make room for people, he would use the terms common among the Outeroos in his present statement, leaving the more minute explanation to be studied in his published report.

He claimed again that man had never been able to work out a civilisation without the use of tameable animals, and many of the Outeroos had been most fortunate in these aids of Nature.

Where man had the association, company and use of the camel, the horse, the ox, the sheep, and the dog, he had been able to keep up the march towards a higher goal. The animals became at once servants, beasts of burden, motive force, food and raiment.

The people about the Mediterranean, for many thousands of years, had all these amiable and useful animals. These animals carried civilisation to the remotest parts of the world, and from servants they became more a source of commerce, food and raiment, than of motive force.

Rearing these animals became the chief industry of Zelania early in her colonial days, for the fertility of the soil, the healthfulness of the country, the geniality of the climate, and the ever reliability of the seasons, made this—of all lands—the most suited for flocks and herds.

"Ah, my children," said Oseba, with animation, "had the Maoris possessed the horse, the ox, and the sheep centuries ago, the dark republic of the South Seas might have sent the most eloquent diplomats to the opulent courts of the Old World—but the Maori was alone."

But let us back to the animals—and "boil them down." These 800,000 Zelanians have 20,250,000 sheep, 1,360,000 cattle, 280,000 horses, and 224,000 swine; and—well, there are a few thousand, more or less, dogs. These 20,000,000 sheep are of a fine breed, reared with the dual idea of good wool and good mutton; they belong to about 19,000 persons, and they yield, from export, an annual income of about £5,000,000. There are 11,700 flocks of less than 500 per flock, and 138 of over 20,000. The Zelanians confess to having the best mutton in the world.

I quote:—

"Zelania is a country of big things, only when taken on the average. She has no millionaires and no paupers. She has no sheep kings or sheep thieves. She has big geysers, and big Premiers, big yields, big people and big ideas, but few big fortunes. They have 'trusts' in Zelania, but they are in God and—the people."

PROFITABLE EXERCISE.

Among the most pleasant as well as most profitable industries anywhere, I conclude from the notes, are dairying and fruit-growing, and Mr. Oseba thinks that in no country or climate on the upper crust of our planet are these industries more promising or more profitable, especially the former. The absence of cold winters, the purity of the atmosphere, the nutritiousness of the grasses, and the frequency of rain, all "work together for good" to those who attend to business.

I quote:—

"The relative area of land in Zelania specially suitable for this purpose is enormous, and as the fertility of the soil is improved instead of being impoverished by this industry, the possibilities of its development are incalculable.

"For a person with moderate means this seems the most tempting industry in this charming land. Mining, too, with its variety of products, the generous laws, the healthful climate, the abundance of water, is a most interesting and remunerative industry.

"The mining laws and regulations are as generous as the land laws, and in every undertaking of this nature the policy of the Government is, 'arm energy with the implements of industry that wealth may come in response to the kindly invitation.'

"As the Zelanians were among the most commercial people of the globe, considering population, they entered into the spirit of railway building in early times with great enthusiasm. The railway mania began during the reign of provincialism, and each province commenced its little system without regard to the plans of the others."

Here a map was thrown on the wall, showing different railway systems, with their different routes and purposes. Considering the nearness of the sea to every populous centre, and the accessibility of these points for steamers, the construction of costly railways evidenced a commendable spirit of enterprise.

Doubtless, provincial pride and a willingness to bid high for population in former times, that rents on fine estates might be raised, had much to do in stimulating this enterprise.

The railway lines were expensive, but they have proved a good investment. I conclude that at present Zelania has 2,325 miles of railway. The road-bed is good, the rolling-stock fair; travelling is about as comfortable as in other countries, and the average passenger fare is lower than in America. For the benefit of the joint owners—the people—all "profits" go to the general lowering of rates.

The wisdom of the Australasian colonies in constructing, managing, and owning the transportation lines cannot be too much admired, Mr. Oseba thinks, especially as it was "contrary to the world's experience."

The orator argued logically, and in detail, the wisdom of the public ownership of public utilities, claiming that, as transportation was of so vital an importance to all commercial people, unless the Government owned and operated the railways, the railways would, by some means, own and operate the Government.

"Hongi," Maori Salutation.

He proceeded:—

"The railways in Zelania are a valuable asset. Their construction has doubled the value of the public lands, and, as at cheap rates they are yielding a good per cent. on the total cost, they are worth to-day the full amount of the investment.

"The railways are being extended and improved as rapidly as the demands require, and the finances justify; and with the post offices, telegraphs and telephones, they are under the watchful eye and control of a Cabinet Minister—at present Sir Joseph Ward—the early evidence of whose sagacity was shown in his having selected these antipodean regions as a country in which to endure life's fitful dream.

"Sir Joseph is an ornament too, as well as a pillar in, the political and social structure of Zelania. He is affable, polished, ambitious and patriotic. He is brilliant in his business conceptions, and, possessing a pleasing personality and persuasive speech, he rarely fails in the execution of his well organised designs. While he has hardly passed the noon of life, he has long been the skilful lieutenant of the sturdy Seddon, and if the chief, at whose side he has so unfalteringly stood, should weary under the burden of public cares, it would seem most fitting that the mantle of leadership should fall upon the trained shoulders of this able and versatile statesman.

"Then the construction of all the railways, with all their *et ceteras*—the highways, bridges, and other public works—is also directed by a Cabinet Minister.

"Well, from all the 'millions' that have been spent under this tireless guardian in the promotion of these stupendous improvements, in a country, too, in which very many intelligent people would sit up 'all hours' to find something to criticise, there is probably not one person who could be persuaded that there was ever a sixpence coined in His Majesty's Mint sufficiently nimble to find its way into the wrong pocket.

"This 'Minister of Works' works twice as many hours per day as any one of the thousands of men in his employ, and the thought of his being influenced by any consideration save that of the public good, could not be advanced to the debatable stage in any company in Zelania. These people trust their 'servants,' and rarely, indeed, is their trust betrayed. This is a Zelanian 'trust.'

"Nearly all these great works are carried on under a co-operative policy, with a wage based on individual capacity to earn, the work being usually given to the 'unemployed' nearest the productive operations. It is claimed that this policy has been no more costly than the old contract system. It is of the people, for the people, by the people.

'Who will not sing "God Save the King"
Shall hang as high's the steeple.
But while we sing "God Save the King,"
We'll ne'er forget the people.'"

Here, the notes record, the poetess Vauline suggested that the sage Oseba give the audience a little further information regarding Zelanian statesmen, their relation to the Motherland, and their hold upon the affections of the people.

In interesting detail, Mr. Oseba explained that while Zelania claimed allegiance to the British Crown, and that in defence of Britain's honor she would pour out her blood and treasure with Spartan valor, she was so proudly free that should the same "loved mother" demand a penny per pound tax on her tea, the next rising sun would kiss a thousand emblems of a new-born republic. For the Motherland, Zelania would sacrifice all—save honor—but it must be as a partner, and not as a vassal.

"I have no desire," said the orator, "to applaud the star performers of this great social drama, for such leaders are but the chosen instruments of the people, and as no other power had conspicuously succeeded in establishing justice among men, the people have the innings, and may—yea, must—be trusted.

"But the chosen are not sure to enjoy the 'affections of all,' for as long as a man is alive and in business," Mr. Oseba concludes, "there will be marked differences of opinion regarding his mental and moral worth."

Mr. Oseba "caught on" alright, for he soon discovered that among the Outeroos the real live man is always in somebody's way; that the fellow who reached the persimmons, or "got there"—at the top of the poll—was bad, and that if such a one ever did a proper thing it was through inadvertence, or from unholy motives.

While a man "is quite alive" and wants something, we scoff at his ability, we laugh at his language, we question his motives, and we wound him with our poisoned shafts. But let him die once, and what a wondrous change! As long as he is in our way, as long as his quivering heart can feel, we cannonade him; then, when we have wrapped him in the habiliments of eternal silence, we feel subdued, we magnify his virtues, and—*canonise* him.

Among a free and educated people, on questions of domestic policy, there are always differences of opinion among men, and this is no imputation either on the intelligence or the patriotism of the disputants; but Mr. Oseba rather likes the man who gets there while the other fellow is holding his caucus.

From these opposing opinions arise party prejudices and factional strife, and earnestness should be reckoned a virtue, even should the reasoning finally prove faulty. Democracy, then, instead of raising men above the human, not infrequently reminds us how far men fall short of the divine.

But on this point Mr. Oseba closes thus:—

"While Zelania is a conspicuous jewel of the British Crown and very red on the map, and her government is of, for, and by the people, any praise of her statesmen is a compliment to the character and intelligence of the 'ultimate power'—the people."

LET'S TO BUSINESS.

Here, for the sake of brevity, I condense many eloquent pages, and for the sake of clearness I make Mr. Oseba's story my own, quoting when we pass the general argument.

Commercially, I conclude, Zelania, on a population basis, is one of the leading countries on the upper crust, her annual exports and imports amounting to about £24,000,000. To furnish financial convenience for the great industrial and commercial enterprise of the country, there are provided excellent banking facilities. As a fact, the capital invested in banking, for so small a society, seems fabulous. The banking laws are explicit, and while the banks have provided for their own perfect safety, they cannot, if they should desire, oppress the people. But the fact that advances by these banks amount to about £20 per cap. of the whole people shows to what extent they are patronised.

Referring to a review of the political side of this country, it appears that the Zelanians, all in all, have the most rational system of taxation of any people anywhere. With a desire to encourage "home industry," and also influenced by custom, the laws provide that the necessary revenue be raised by the usual methods, direct and indirect taxation, but it is of the former I shall chiefly speak. Of the total, say £3,113,000, about 74 per cent. is raised by indirect methods, or from taxes on imports and excises, while 26 per cent. is raised by a direct tax on land and income.

On land and income the taxes are graduated, the rates increasing with the increase of the income, or the value of the estate—those on land being on the unimproved value. This system of graduated taxation is a new departure, a reversal of the history of the ages. It is based upon the idea of social defence of personal rights. It is plain that the more property a person possesses the greater are his claims upon society for protection, and the graduated tax is simply demanding extra rent for extra room, or extra charge for the extra expense for the extra security given. In fact, it is extra insurance for extra risks.

The justice of the idea has been clear to thoughtful men—who had nothing to tax—for many years; but in Zelania—to discover a new truth means to occupy a new position. Zelania does not allow her intellectual jewels to rust in the brains of the academician.

Under Zelania's novel policy the books show her to be carrying a public debt greater in proportion to population than any other country, but for every shilling of her debt she has more than two shillings in valuable assets, and for most of it she has a reproductive asset. So, as a fact, the burden helps to carry the people. Like other "heavily involved" Australasian States, if measured by the rule of other nations, she is among the least burdened of all people.

"And these people were cunning in handicraft."

Oseba tells his audience at some length about the manufacturing industries of Zelania, but a small space will suffice, as it is better to remember the haste of the age. The pith is, that considering the newness of the country, and the narrow limits of the markets, there has been a laudable advance in manufacturing enterprise. The chief industries, of course, have developed from the most common and profitable material resources of the country.

"My children," said Oseba, "we are never done with Zelania's wonders. While she offers the most tempting rewards for effort, she gives nothing ready-made. In all Zelania there was, and is, nothing of the 'Arise, Peter, slay and eat' to be found, but everywhere there is seen: 'In my treasure-house there are many jewels, and he who cannot open my door and unlock my chest would be an unsafe custodian of my riches, an unworthy recipient of my favors.' Or, like the gay and mischievous maiden who says, 'Catch me, and you have a kiss,' she keeps all her promises. Relying on Nature without effort, any man in Zelania might genteelly starve; but relying on effort with Nature's aid, any man in Zelania may live like a prince.

"Zelania had no indigenous animals, and really no indigenous grasses, and her fruits were meagre, but she had the magic force of fecundity, and she said:—

'I am the nourisher. Like the wise virgins
I have long waited a worthy wooer.
By action, arose I from the mad seas' bosom.
By action, arose my heaven-piercing mountains.
By action, were my rivers dug, and plains fertilised.
By action, created I and concealed my mineral wealth;
And, loving "action," to him who gives an ounce of sweat,
I pledge a pound of glittering gold.'

"Yes, as Zelania's laws give pound for pound of private contribution to worthy causes, so Zelania's goddess of fortune gives to honest toil a reward of many fold.

"Zelania offers nothing for sloth, everything for industry. Her treasures are all hidden, but a plough reveals them. Tickle a field with a harrow, and it laughs with a crop of a hundred bushels to the acre. Remove a fern, a sprig of clover comes. Bring a little rabbit to 'amuse the boys,' and, lo! Nature is so pleased that the 'boys' have to hustle to save the crops.

"Well, as Zelania, by every feature of her nature, suggests action, her people are exploring every field of industrial enterprise. Though wages are high and the market for most of the manufactured goods very limited, there has been reasonable success in many branches of the arts productive.

"Of course, the chief of these industries," he says, "relate to what might be called raw pastoral products: meat, wool, butter, and cheese. The list of manufactures include some twenty general classes, covering over one hundred sub-classes.

"As a rule, the manufacturing plants are fairly well equipped—the machinery for the meat and dairy works being especially up to date. The wages of the 41,000 persons employed are, high. Nearly £8,000,000 are invested in plant, and the annual output amounts to £17,000,000. Certainly these facts speak strongly for the enterprise of so new a people.

"But, Zelania, 'twas not thy 'riches' nor thy trade,
'Twas not thy fields, thy fruits, thy wool that made
Thee loved of gods and men, nor gold; nor stately domes.
'Twas 'justice,' inscribed on the portals of thy homes.
For thou first learned that men and women must be great,
Else folly only boasts the grandeur of a State."

SCENE VIII.—Act IV.

THE MORAL SIDE.

RELATING to the moral side of Zelania's progress, the notes were very full, but the story will be briefly and chiefly told in the less chaste style of Marmaduke:—

As a rule, the people of Zelania, if the great discoverer is correct, enjoy excellent health—or should enjoy it—though we rarely "enjoy" anything that is very common. Of course, Zelania has not yet evolved a type, though she has begun her task, for while the Zelanians are of excellent stock, the "born Zelanian" is said to be superior, both in physical fibre and mental perception, to the average person of the Motherland. Nature, Mr. Oseba thinks, will preserve the "sorrel hair," the white skin, the florid complexion, the fine shoulders and the firm "understanding."

The Zelanians are loyal to the Motherland. They speak of Britain as "Home," and, as a compliment to her, the color with which she paints her dependencies is conspicuously present in the cheeks of Zelanian ladies.

Unless Zelania dilutes her blood by hurried accessions to her population, she will, in a few generations, furnish the finest type of mental and physical man and womanhood that ever kicked a football, or "did the block," on the surface of Oliffa.

Maori Wharepuni.

In the care of the unfortunate, the deaf, the dumb, the blind, and the lunatics, Zelania is already on the "fortunate" side, as Mr. Oseba abundantly testifies.

Oseba says:—

"As an evidence of the satisfaction of the people of Zelania with their present condition, it is only necessary to remark the low death rate among the people. This for the last eleven years has averaged less than ten persons per thousand. For the same period, the rates in Denmark, Norway, and Sweden, were about sixteen per thousand; in the United Kingdom, over eighteen per thousand; in Germany and France, about twenty-two per thousand; in Italy, about twenty-five; and in Austria, over twenty-seven per thousand. Then it appears that of all people the Zelanians are best satisfied with their present situation.—Mayhap, some tarry even a little too long.

"While these people are all earnest, and want to go to heaven—afterwhile— they seem to be in no hurry about starting, and have little desire for risking climatic changes.

"With other matchless wonders, had Nature been attending properly to business, she would have placed the 'Fountain of Youth' in some of these charming spots, for the 'untimely taking off' of a person in Zelania seems quite unjustifiable. A person willingly leaving any other country might be justified in making the change, but when anyone permanently retires from Zelania it means there has been coercion, an exercise of some extraneous power.

"Strange, but the books show seventy-nine suicides to have been committed in one year in Zelania, though it seems incredible that any person in Zelania should voluntarily retire. Of course, they may have desired to get to heaven ahead of some of their neighbors, for in Zelania they like to be considered a little advanced.

"To insure or secure the public health, there are wise sanitary laws, charitable institutions and hospitals; the practice of medicine is wisely guarded, and carried on by able physicians. In all these public affairs, the Government— which means the people in their organised capacity—is most generous in its assistance.

"In local hospitals, or charitable enterprise, the Government usually gives pound for pound for all private contributions, and the many institutions of the kind in all Australasia furnish a pleasing surprise to observing travellers."

"ON THE MAKE."

Mr. Oseba was greatly interested in the "enterprise" of the Outeroos. I quote:—

"I have visited all the countries of the upper crust of Oliffa, and I have observed that the Outeroos are taking a lot of physical exercise. They are engaged in a mad scramble for dollars. Just why any man should want so many 'dollars' is not very clear, but it is very clear that they do want them. Men with very many dollars are, in most things, much like the men with very few dollars; they are alarmed at smallpox, the cold and the heat make them thirsty, and the shapely actress turns alike their shallow heads. Then, too, the grim chariot that carries waste from the 'City of Confusion' and deposits it in the 'City of the Silent,' calls about as promptly at the mansion of Lady Bountiful as at the hovel of the laundress.

"When the man of dollars dies, he is about as dead as his footman—under like circumstances. He'll be dead about as long, and whatever his facilities for the transfer of wealth while in active business, he can take none of it with him. But, maybe, 'tis well, for if the old story be true, it would probably melt.

"The world has been aroused by the magic force of modern genius, and is being unified by Anglo-Saxon commercial enterprise. The nations are growing wealthy; gold is the sole object of ambition, of toil, of production, of trade. For gold the industrious strive, the duke marries, the boss robs, the politician 'negotiates,' the lawyer deceives, the judge decrees, the noble cheats, and the 'parson'—takes up a collection. In this enormous confusion, a great many people get a lot of exercise—a few, 'clip the coupons,' and are happy.

"But the superior Outeroos are only veneered pagans, my children, and gold is the universal god. When Moses smashed the 'golden calf' the fragments must have been many, and each tiny piece must have multiplied into many full-grown bullocks.

"This deity, however, should never grow 'jealous.' His worshippers have at least one sturdy virtue, for among all the millions of them, there kneels not one hypocrite. While the other deities are occasionally scoffed and often neglected, the 'golden calf' is always in evidence. But he attends to business, and in all places he hath wonderful potency.

"Genius has quickened the hand of toil," said Oseba, "but it has not removed the callous, and almost everywhere on the surface of Oliffa the opulence of the mansion tells the wretchedness of the hovel. The owner of the one schemes, the tenant of the other toils. The man who toils, toils for another; the man who 'schemes'—well, the other fellow goes to him for a cheque at the end of the week. Until the great democracies of the Antipodes were established, every government of the world, regardless of title, style or form, conspired with cunning to rob credulity, with the schemer to rob the toiler.

"I have thus reasoned, my children, that you might realise by 'looking upon this picture and then upon this,' that Zelania has introduced to the world a social policy under which the people, in their organised capacity, have secured to the people, in their individual capacity, a fuller measure of the fruits of their mental and physical efforts than was ever enjoyed in any other country under the sun.

"It is not even a policy of the 'greatest good to the greatest number,' for, as the purest happiness consists in a participation of the general joy, it is a policy of the greatest good to all.

"Zelania's motto is: 'He who earns shall have, and he who strives shall enjoy.' In this, the people builded better than they knew, and soon Zelania will be the most conspicuously conspicuous spot on Oliffa, and thousands of people will visit her marvellous shores, not more to enjoy the museums of the gods than to study the customs and the character of the first nation of emancipated men.

"Zelania, though she is now the foremost among the world's social pioneers, was practically wrested from Nature by the present generation of men. The Zelanian Isles were Nature's last best gift to the noblest race of her noblest creatures—the gods seeming to have waited for a proper tenantry for these more than Elysian fields.

"Zelania, my children, is the John in the Wilderness—the prophesied of old, the prophet of the new. She is the beacon of the present, the divine torch of the future."

Oh, that is inspiring! Let's take an amateur "soar."

To the Goddess of Justice their prayers are read.
To that Goddess Zelanians bow low the head;
For she gave the Zelanians, nor seer nor priest,
She gave them the custom of Galilee's feast.
For rich though her gifts to the present and past,
She saved for these Britons the "best for the last."

Here built they a temple—'twas built on the plan
That he is most noble that's most of a man;
They laid as foundations the "love of their kind";
For strength of the structure, firm held they in mind
That no fortune or creed, but justice alone,
Should ever remain as the chief corner stone.

They builded the temple—'twas builded by men

Who were called from the shop, from the mountain and glen.
'Twas builded for men—not for some, as of yore—
'Twas builded of men, from the spires to the floor.
'Twas builded too strong for the strong to transgress,
But 'twas builded too weak, the most weak to oppress.

Pardon; let's back to Leo's notes, for Mr. Oseba's modest candour better suits this prosy age.

SHE CAME—FINALLY.

"And the Lord God said, 'It is not well that man should be alone; I will make him a help-meet for him.'"

Without irreverence, I would regard this as an excellent idea.

Mr. Oseba, say the notes, gave a most pleasing review of the domestic relations of the Outeroos, with special reference to the position of women.

The notes on this pleasing phase of the oration were full and spirited, but in boiling down some dozen pages I will array the orator's impressions in my own garb, as though I myself had learned something on this interesting theme.

The stronger and more haughty among the Outeroos are called men, while the more frail, gentle and loquacious are called wo-man, which means that in some way these latter are to be "wooed and won" before reaching the final end of existence.

In old times, man won these fair creatures in a race for life. They "wooed them" with a bludgeon, captured, and dragged them to a hut, and chained them to the door-post until they were "persuaded" to stew the oysters. But this woman, with a shrewdness she is said to have retained even to this day, cunningly devised a trap into which she knew her "lord and master"—an epithet that has survived the wreck of empires—would place his brogan.

From the waste of the "kitchen" she fertilised the soil at the roots of a heavy grass, and it grew into a grain. She moistened a plant, and it opened into a fruit. She tamed the young animal—brought for the stew—and it became the faithful dog. By a cushion of moss she softened the log used by her lord as a pillow, and, on his return with terrapin and salmon berries, she looked into his swarthy face and smiled.

He was impressed. He took her gently by the hand, pressed her to his palpitating bosom, and, looking into her deep liquid eyes, he said, "I love you." He broke the chains that bound her, and, the wrist fetters being stubborn, he polished them into bracelets—and these are still worn as a rudiment of the earlier times. What "Papa" might say came later. The twain became one flesh—which one, has always been debatable.

Then it was arranged, with very considerable limitation, that they should be partners. She, the wooed-man, or woman, was to love, to serve, to obey, while he—furnished the superintendence.

The old system dropped out of use many centuries ago, and the new was a change, largely in form, hardly in fact.

The old fetters have rusted in the museums of the past. The club, that potent persuader of old, has been presented to the champion of the base-ball team, and the woman is at large. But as the priest now signs and sanctifies the bond, the change, in most countries, is still chiefly in the character of the fetters.

All people have traditions that help to justify the stronger in acts of oppression, and to conciliate the weaker in their vassalage.

But civilisation has grown—only with the emancipation of women. Just as the fetters have been removed from the brain, and soul, and conscience of woman, has the social ideal risen, has arbitrary force weakened, and have feeling and reason prevailed. The woman is the mother; from hereditary and prenatal influences come form and character.

How can a mother, with the feeling of inferiority, a feeling of subdued dependence, with no courage nor conscious individuality, bring forth brave, independent, high-minded offspring? Only by emancipated mothers can full-statured men be reared, and thus has the race crawled slowly forward.

For the snail-like pace of human progress, the world is more indebted to the past and political inequalities of the sexes than to all other retarding influences combined.

With the progress of science, with the physical forces of Nature harnessed by mental exploits, the relative positions of human muscle and human sentiment are changing, and, with a cultured reason, deeper affections and higher ideals invariably appear.

Champagne Caldron at Wairakei, near Taupo.

Here I quote:—

"In Zelania, women are 'people,'" said Mr. Oseba, "and liberty and social rights are not limited to any particular cut of the garments. In Zelania, the mother, the wife, and the daughter stand proudly erect with the father, the husband, and the brother—and still the seasons come and go, the showers are as usual damp, the fruits ripen in due course of time, the fair 'fellow-elector' is as greatly surprised at the suddenness of the long-hoped-for question, papa is invoked as of yore, and the gay old world swings merrily on her uneventful voyage.

"In Zelania, my children, the women vote, and claim equal political rights with those who buy the opera tickets and set up the ice cream. Of course, they don't go to Parliament, save at the sittings, to which they bring their loving smiles and their sewing but they are on their way, and they will get there all the same.

"But with the coming of women few changes have been noted—so few of the hopes or fears of the ages have been realised. Woman does not wear spurs—she has not got out of her place—and she does not do the sights, as does her hubby, and swear she was detained at the 'ledger.' She has not become masculine, for she is still the gentle mother of the children, and she is still the same dear old mother, or wife, sister, or lover as of yore, when Zeus said, 'Behold! when the fair smile, victory is nigh.'

"But neither have all the hopes, so confidently cherished, been fully realised. It has not been discovered—so 'tis said—that the 'political atmosphere' has materially changed; that legislators are greatly altered in personal character; that social ethics have been revolutionised; or, to the surprise of many, that the distance between drinks has been materially lengthened. But, whatever the means, great changes come slowly.

"As a fact, the experience of Zelania, at three parliamentary elections, rather indicates that on social, political, economic, and moral questions, the men and women of the country are 'tarred' with about the same brush.

"But in this reform there is a sense of justice and a conscious largeness of soul that is mentally exhilarating, and must result favorably to society everywhere. In the air of Zelania all fetters rust away, and the flag of a new victory, won over traditional custom and selfishness, having been unfurled in this noble land, people afar will first dream, then hesitate, then inquire, and then conclude to have a reshuffling of the cards in this doubtful game of life."

INTELLECTUAL TASTES.

"If Zelania is proud of her system of education, she may be forgiven," was Oseba's first reference to the intellectual ambition of her people. He was eloquent on this subject. As any thinker could "guess," the Zelanians were certainly not slow in efforts to elevate the mental tastes or in making provisions for the education of the future citizens.

The foundation of the present excellent school system was laid by the old provincial authorities, and the best hopes of the pioneers, those who believed in "teaching the young ideas how to shoot," are being beautifully realised.

The orator says:—

"At present 82 per cent. of the people of Zelania have the rudiments of education, which, considering the pioneer character of the country, 'speaks volumes' for the community.

"There are over 2,000 schools in the colony, with an attendance of about 150,000 pupils. Of these schools some 1,600 are free, and all children from seven to fourteen years of age are required to attend them. The natives, also, are supplied with 96 of these free primary schools, at which 4,500 pupils attend. Rather new; but the railways carry the children free to and from the nearest school.

"In the primary schools, besides the usual branches, such as reading, writing, arithmetic, geography, grammar, and history, the elementary sciences, and drawing, the girls are taught sewing and domestic economy, and the boys are drilled as 'military heroes.'

"Besides these free primary schools there are many higher secondary schools, supported partly by the Government and partly by 'fees,' and many more private and denominational schools of a very good order. As a rule, one religious denomination—the Roman Catholics—decline to very generally patronise the public schools, and this church supports independently a large number of excellent educational institutions. There are eight technical or art schools, at which some 3,000 young persons attend, a majority of them finishing their school life at this stage. The branches taught at these schools, and the subjects of examination, cover a broad field, and the young person who becomes proficient in them may be regarded as fairly well equipped for most of the battles of this active age. At these schools a young person is armed with the 'practical,' with little danger of being over 'stuffed.'

"As a fact, my children," said Mr. Oseba, "many countries on the upper crust are filled with educated dunces, who are mentally deformed by over-cramming, and who are inspired by the hopes of living on 'sheepskin'; but as Zelania has practically no rich or leisured class, the basic idea of school-day training is to fit the rising generation, not for ornamental, but for practical service.

"Zelania, as a capstone of her educational edifice, has a university, which was instituted by Act of Parliament in 1874, not for the purpose of teaching, but for encouraging a liberal education. This university is an examining, scholarship-awarding, and degree-granting institution, and the responsibility for the success of university work rest mainly with the four affiliated teaching colleges, which have a curricula in science, arts, medicine, law, mining, engineering and agriculture.

"Then there are industrial schools, schools for the blind, deaf, and dumb, which, taken all in all, constitute a splendid system, all being carried on at heavy expense to the State. But the general high character of the people, their usual bearing and manners, the average moral tone, and absence, in the main, of coarseness and vulgarity, tell strongly for the merits of the educational system of the country, as well as for the natural and social influences that mould society."

OTHER "TASTES."

With the next phase of Zelanian life, according to the notes of Leo Bergin, Oseba was deeply impressed and pleased, for he said:—

"As might be expected, my children, in a land so blessed by Nature, occupied by so noble a race, and ruled by such incomparably wise and generous laws, the word 'pauper' is not found in Zelanian statistics, and the 'criminals,' considering the newness of the country, are few indeed."

Speaking of the character of crime, Oseba said:—

"Vice and virtue, my children, are largely questions of sensation. The actions of men that produce disagreeable sensations—immediate or remote—we call vices, while the opposite we call virtues. We are the product of experience. Vice is the guide board to virtue—the danger signal. Without vice there would be no definition for virtue.

"But taste has much to do in guiding a people. The Zelanians have a taste for knowledge, but they have other tastes. The Christian Outeroos are thirsty, and the Zelanians are Outeroos. Strange, but in a single year there were over 7,000 of these noble Zelanians arrested for their earnest efforts to satisfy this peculiar infatuation. This seems incredible, for while there are several persons in Zelania who are never known to be thirsty, there are about 7,000,000 gallons of beer used annually in filling the 'alimentary canal' of the Zelanians. Just why, with so goodly a supply, with so short a distance, both in time and space, between drinks, this peculiar sensation should turn the heads of men, is not very clear.

"Many very well-meaning people believe there would be less 'arrests' for these peculiar freaks should the distance between drinks be extended, but others, having considerable interest in the matter, hold that most of these confused persons are 'taken in' during their long search for somebody to do the 'shouting.'

"However," Oseba said, "there is a pleasing side, for while 51 per cent. of the population over fifteen years of age were born in Zelania, this portion is said to have furnished but 17 per cent. of the Court's takings for this confusing recreation.

"For other crimes, the 51 per cent. of native-born furnish but 28 per cent. of the law breakers.

"It may be, my children, that the 49 per cent. of the foreign born, who are said to furnish the other per cent. of the 'takings,' are only celebrating their arrival in so glorious a country—a country in which a day's earnings, it is said, will pay for many beers. At any rate, the native-born Zelanian seems the better man, for he either 'calls' less frequently or 'carries his load' better than the 'new chum.'"

But all are thirsty, Mr. Oseba, and the "practice at the bar," if not profitable, is exhilarating.

They think they want a drink.
When it's wet they want a drink.
When it's dry they want a drink.
When it's warm, and when it's cold;
When they're young and when they're old—
They think, and when they think,
They want a drink.
When they're sick, and when they're well,
Bound for heaven or for ——,
Then they think—they want a drink.
But do they think when e'er they drink?
Or does the drink confuse the think?

"But the fact," said Mr. Oseba, "that in one year there were twelve homicides is most surprising to the inquiring stranger. Surely no man well 'quartered' in Zelania should care to be killed, and the reckless head that would plan, or the ruthless hand that would execute a design to close a life in Zelania, should in some manner be restrained from so fell a purpose. Deducting the homicides of foreign birth, however, it leaves for the Zelanians the cleanest record in the 'Christian' world—as one would expect.

"The Zelanians, my children, are usually glad they are alive, and, too, they are usually willing to allow others to remain and enjoy the entertainment."

INTELLECTUAL GYMNASTICS.

The notes relating to Zelanian art and literature were very full, and they were complimentary. 'Tis said that art develops only with age, and that while the aspect of Nature may appeal to the poetic or artistic imagination, art arises from dominant ideas, from deeply-seated sentiments, and as in new, active, progressive, and commercial countries the dominant ideas do not lend themselves to reverie, and could not be feelingly expressed on canvas, art in

Zelania must be "imported" for a season. But literature has come, and literature is civilisation.

The notes continue:—

"Literature, or, to broaden the theme and say the taste for knowledge and for general reading in Zelania, deserves many compliments. While there is not, as yet, a literature bearing a distinctive stamp of Zelanian genius, many volumes with real merit, both in prose and verse, have been written, and the topics show a versatile taste, knowledge, and imagination.

"While from the very nature of things Zelania must be a land of romance, poesy, and song, of the stage, of the race, and the hall, yet from the sturdiness of the stock there must first come a sufficiency of works of a graver character as the present exuberance of society tones down toward restful meditation. To-day Zelania is 'waltzing,' to-morrow she will walk, and next week she will think.

"Zelania has many well-managed libraries, and, considering the population, the Zelanians buy, pay for, and read, more books than any other people on earth. The kind of books? Well, just the kind that any student would expect—trash, the most of it, as trashy trash is the taste of the times, everywhere.

Silica Terraces, Orakei Korako, between Rotorua and Taupo.

"But it shows the desire for reading, and, as these children grow older, a more sober class of books will find its way from the shelves to the desk of the reader. Even now in Zelania the taste for blood and thunder literature is waning, while gay and chaste humour, with glimpses of the philosophy of life, is in growing favor. The heart of a nation may be seen through its laws, but the heart, and the soul, and the laws are the product of national literature. Literature is civilisation.

"The Zelanians are a new community—the people have but recently come together—society is in a 'stew,' as the members have but little mutual 'acquaintance,' and as the new environment, the air, and the aspect of Nature suggest hilarity, all the sermonising in the world would not convert this Zelanian 'holiday' into a prayer-meeting. In the Zelanian character there appears the sparkling diamond, and in the Zelanian fibre there are also the oak and the steel that will tell in the morrows.

"As an evidence of the mental appetite, or the reading habit, the 800,000 Zelanians have and support 200 newspapers, several of which rank with the great journals of the globe, and the average tone of no press in the world is higher than that of Zelania.

"True to the racial defects," Oseba said, "the Zelanians, like the Australians and the Americans, are not linguists. These wonderful people seem neither desirous nor capable of speaking 'strange tongues.' With brief experience, I thought this unfortunate, but I gradually changed my mind, for not only is the world coming to the use of the English speech,[C] but as 'silence is golden,' and it is manifestly easier to keep quiet in one than in several languages, this weakness has a virtuous side.

"I have often noticed while abroad how prone are the masters of many tongues, when striving to keep silent in one, to break out in some less euphoneous speech, and thus give themselves away, or at least arouse a contagious smile of good-natured disapproval.

"But mental gymnastics in Zelania have produced a high order of visible results.

"Though the country is very new in all phases of modern being, political, social, judicial, educational and religious, it possesses a wonderfully symmetrical form. For its present splendid condition the country is indebted to the efforts of men who were themselves the products of hard but happy and interesting colonial life.

"New and distant as this country is, narrow as has been the political, industrial and social horizon, by the vigor of inherited pluck and the resistless persuasiveness of the romantic environment, in physical courage, in moral stamina and in intellectual force, Zelania's leading men will compare well with those trained in the great world's historic centres.

"The present Premier, who has guided the ship of State during more than ten years of its most wonderful progress, graduated in the rugged school of industrial activity, and, casting off the implements of custom and delusion, he not only made Zelania a more conspicuously red patch on the world's map, but himself became a recognised force in the Councils of Empire.

"But with others than her progressive statesmen, Zelania is rich in sturdy manhood and ability—grey matter. Her schools and colleges rank well with the educational institutions of older and richer countries; her instructors are profoundly learned; her judiciary, with its present head, would adorn the bench of the Motherland itself; and her professionals in law and medicine, if cast in a body in any other country, would not lower the average.

"Of course, my children, as yet not all the milestones are statues; not all who loaf in the parks are poets, nor are all who stroll in the streets philosophers, but according to the prevailing notion in Zelania, this noble aspiration will soon be realised.

"These, my children, though I drank not with the statesmen, I came not before the courts, I 'feed' no solicitor, and my health was perfect during my sojourn in Zelania, were my impressions on these themes."

FOR OPINION'S SAKE.

"Let your light so shine before men, that they may see your good works." (Usually obeyed.—ED.)

Under this head the notes were full and clear, but as life grows shorter and space less, I will condense greatly.

Amoora Oseba informs his audience that the Zelanians have considerable religion—in fact, there seems to be nearly enough to go round, for all save a very few are reported to have it in some of its various forms.

"Of the 800,000 people, nearly all," he says, "belong to some religious society, and about all who claim God as a father, seem to think it necessary to regard the church as a mother—so few do business direct.

"Of the various creeds, the Church of England claims about 40 per cent. of the whole; the Presbyterian 22; and the Roman Catholic, 14 per cent. There are nearly 1,000 clergymen in Zelania, said to be gentlemen of excellent attainments.

"As would be expected from so free and civilised a people, there is among all classes and creeds in Zelania a commendable spirit of common brotherhood and toleration. As a fact, members of the various creeds drink at the same bar and attend the same football match, though, being so reared, they desire to go to heaven by different trains. All seem to strive together for the general good, dividing, by common consent, as to methods for the accomplishment of the one desired aim. The Roman Catholics, however, that their followers may be so instructed that they will be sure to 'select the proper train,' usually provide their own schools, while contributing, through general taxation, to the support of most of the others. Probably in no country so universally religious is there so little creed prejudice or intolerance.

"But political and social emancipation everywhere gives a man a conscious dignity and worth that places him in closer harmony with the infinite, and tells for sympathy, love, and charity. The people are religious, but not bigoted. The are religious, but they do not superstitiously cringe, and, as they have been specially guided, they express no disfavor with the methods of the Deity.

"As a fact, like all well regulated people, the Zelanians pray, but, instead of prostrating themselves, they stand bravely erect, and, considering themselves the crowning act of the creative power, they congratulate the Almighty on the excellence of His handiwork."

Here the poetess Vauline inquired if all the people among the superior Outeroos worshipped the same deity.

"Yes, my children," said the sage Oseba, with candor, "on Sundays. On Sundays the Christian Outeroos meet in comfortable places and worship the one true God. On the other days, many people give a lot of attention to another deity. This every-day deity—by persons who praise lavish generosity in other people—is spoken of very slightingly.

"This deity is worshipped by many people under many names, but the Americans, among whom it is said—abroad—he hath great influence, spell it this way—$. It may be doubtful, however, if the Americans really care more for the smiles of this deity than others, but they get up earlier. From tradition the Christian Outeroos call him Mammon, and though he is denounced very much by pious lips, he is considerably in evidence in very holy places.

"Of course, my children, these observations do not apply to the Zelanians. But the Outeroos are growing wiser, stronger, nobler, and better, and the people are inclining to the notion that he who serves man most, pleases God best."

Right, Mr. Oseba! The world grows better, and more truly religious as it grows wiser.

When our skies are filled with demons—
In famine or in feast—
We cower before the lightning,
And we kneel before the priest;
When we grovel in the caverns,
The laying on of hands,
Our service and our substance,
Our faith and fear, commands.
But we peer into the heavens—
Recking not the frown nor rod—
Till we gain a glimpse of Euclid,
Then we're face to face with God.

SCENE VIII.—Act V.

"WORTHY OF HIS HIRE."

And it was decreed that the lives of those who wrought should be spared.

AS Leo Bergin, before he retired, himself took a deep interest in all industrial affairs, he reported Oseba in profusive detail as the labor situation of Zelania was discussed.

There had been an intermission and lunch, and the audience, feeling refreshed, showed deep interest in a problem, the solution of which had taxed the best energies of the ablest statesmen in many countries for many generations. As a text for his pleasing sermon, Oseba said:—

"To you, my children, to the Shadowas of Cavitorus, it will seem strange, but among the Christian Outeroos there is industrial confusion about everywhere, with little prospect of early harmony—for Zelania alone is a land without strikes, without class hatred, and, of those having parliaments, without a labor party in the legislature."

I conclude from the notes:—

Zelania was settled by an excellent class of people, and though too much of the better lands, as before remarked, were at first allowed to fall into few hands, influenced by the isolation and distance from the scenes that created the old precedent, by the novelty of the environment, from the necessities of discovering new expedients to satisfy the new demands or conditions, and from the quickening influence of new competition in a new, free, and exhilarating climate, there was a rush of brains to the head in Zelania, and a new shuffle of the cards was called.

Where none were rich, and all had to hustle, the "grafter" was respected. A community of interests arose, and he who wrote and he who wrought marched shoulder to shoulder, choosing from among themselves the instruments or servants through which the public conscience should find expression in law.

In questions of colonial policy, none invoked the "shades of honored sires," none appealed to the "experience of the ages," none asked or cared what Britain or America was doing, but "how can we construct the most comfortable edifice from the material at hand?" was the problem they sought to solve.

If all those who have prayed, struggled, fought, and died for liberty, from Otanes, the Persian, down to the swarthy sons of Cuba or the Philippines, could behold this scene, they might well say—not in the words of Mr. Oseba—"Lord, now lettest Thou Thy servant depart in peace, for mine eyes have seen Thy salvation."

In Zelania there were no class contests. There was no social revolution in the story, but the people "rose to the occasion," they looked around inquiringly, yielded to the logic of the situation, and—were.

Boiling Fountains, Lake Rotomahana.

Here the people saw clearly the fundamental theory, or basic essentials of production. Here they saw Nature's treasure-house filled with tempting rewards, and they soon realised that toil was the open sesame to which Nature responded promptly, and with a lavish hand.

They saw that "labor and land," after a long divorce, must re-wed—for the children's sake—and that "wealth," instead of being a partial god that sprang from magic caves to aid the cunning in squeezing humanity, was really but the savings or net products of "yesterday's" toil, and capital but that part of wealth devoted to improving the implements with which toil may more easily coin more wealth from the stores of material, offered by Nature free to her inquiring children. Who "corners" the raw material, insults dame Nature, and assassinates liberty.

There being some considerable unanimity of feeling on these questions in Zelania, it was deemed wise to arrange some equitable rules for the working of the various factors, cogs, wheels and pulleys of this complex machine. Of course, a few persons who felt strongly that they were entitled to complimentary passes to all the public entertainments objected; but these gentlemen were asked to stand by and "hold the 'phone" while the inquiry was being made.

Mr. Oseba said: "So near is the Government of Zelania to the doors of the people that the laws are really but the recorded conclusions of the community."

The people had learned—I conclude from the notes—that in all countries and in all ages, a monopolisation of the land with legal privileges had resulted in insolent class distinctions, poverty, misery, and oppression, and they proposed to take up a collection, and erect a new lighting-plant. For—

Not for booty came the Briton, but for a home;
And he built a State, from foundation to dome.
In honor of his sire he "grew." To the "old chimes"
He listened, but he hewed and carved, to fit the "times."
As oracles, he inquired of "Justice." "Glory"
To him was naught, "but works," said he, "live in story."

Mr. Oseba reminded his audience of the rules regulating land tenure and "settlement," which held in view the broadening of the base of the social pyramid, and he said the labor laws were but extending the same principles to other members of the productive or industrial machines.

"The labor laws of Zelania," says he, "are unique; but they are only 'unique' in ignoring the 'experience of darker ages,' in their purpose to equitably distribute the burdens and profits of industry, and in the desire of the framers to secure permanent industrial peace and intelligent social co-operation.

"The labor laws of Zelania may be said to be but rules provided for the better understanding between, and the better security of the employer and employee, as joint promoters of industrial enterprise, and nowhere is the holder of wealth given an undue advantage over the creator of wealth.

"The labor legislation of Zelania comprises about thirty-five distinct Acts, and in tone they are usually almost more advisory than mandatory. There are no general laws regulating the hours of labor, or providing a minimum wage, but in the interest of open-handed justice, certain courts may exercise considerable power when called upon to settle questions of this character.[D] The labor legislation began in Zelania as early as 1865, in 'The Master and Apprentice Act,' and has at least kept pace with the rational demands of the community ever since.

"The labor laws of Zelania, like her industries, have grown gradually with the country's requirements, as suggested by the industrial unfoldment of the country. As it is an industrial and commercial community, the laws are designed to cover every phase of business activity, to be specific in their directions, simple in their application, and speedy and inexpensive in their execution."

Uttering a truth, but possibly misquoting, Mr. Oseba remarked:—

"As a despairing statesman once said, 'Rome realises no danger, nay, she heeds no warning, until the enemy is thundering at her gates, when she must act without deliberation,' so, in like manner, the industrial Acts of other countries are usually formulated and passed to meet pressing emergencies, while the sagacity of Zelania prepares, not for emergencies, but that emergencies may not arise.

"While labor is the chief factor in the production of all wealth, from a time to which the 'memory' of man runneth not to the contrary, the select few, who cunningly possessed themselves of the wealth, have treated with scant courtesy those who created it.

"In Zelania, this 'time-honored custom' has been changed, for it has been ordained that he who coins his sweat into the things that administer to human wants, shall not be forgotten by those who coin their cunning into magnets for drawing the price of those things to their commodious pockets.

"In Zelania, my children, people who toil, who build houses, make corkscrews, and grow asparagus, are regarded as considerably human, even outside of Sunday-school and prayer meeting.

"Here the power of one to toil and to produce is considered his capital. His family, in whom the community has an interest, is to be considered and supported from this source, and, if in the employ of another, such a person meets with—or is overtaken by—an accident—his capital impaired—he must be 'compensated.'[E] This, for a time, seemed a hardship on employers—all changes being hardships—but experience has proven otherwise, for the practice not only produced a nobler 'fellow-feeling,' but mutual interest between the employer and the employed.

"Every change necessitates other changes, and every new light exposes some defects that call for improvement.

"In this measure there was a glimpse of justice, but to obviate apparent hardships, the State undertook to insure the laborer, and then it was seen that private companies could find a lot of—financially—healthy exercise in the same line, and thus the industrial machine became more symmetrical.[F]

"To the casual observer, or to him who regards the torch-bearer as an innovator luring away his fetish, and to the wise-looking owl that sits on the cemetery gate hooting at the passing train of progress, these novel experiments seem mischievous and revolutionary; but in the early future, the long-eared politicians of many lands will have to face the inquiry, 'What has made Zelania the industrial paradise of the world? Give us a smile from her canteen.'

"She is changing the ideal, she is blessing the brick and the mortar of which the Temple of State is built.

"If the State is made for woman and for man,
You should make the man and woman—best you can.

"The fact that for a dozen years, the industrial machine of Zelania has worked smoothly, and that, while in other lands there has been much confusion, she has enjoyed an era of unparalleled progress and prosperity, should be some answer to the fears of those who, because 'of old' they made much gains in furnishing Diana with her stage outfit, are now feeling weary.

"However, should these laws fail to satisfy the aspirations of an educated people," Mr. Oseba argued, "the agents of the ultimate authority would be instructed to adjust them to the popular needs of society, and the new patents would be issued.

"As a fact, of all people the Zelanians alone receive as much from, as they contribute to, their Government.

"I am not sure my children, not very sure, that in all cases these liberal laws have quickened the employee's stroke. I am not sure that all employees are endowed with sufficient grey matter to appreciate the fact that every security or privilege conferred by law imposes reciprocal obligations. To emancipate a man, should ennoble him.

"A free man should scorn to soil his palm with an unearned penny. The law that raised the eyes of labor did not intend to direct them to the face of the town clock, and the law that forbade an employer demanding twenty shillings worth of work for fourteen shillings in truck goods, never meant that labor should take from its employer a gold sovereign for fourteen shillings' worth of work.

"Justice and security should elevate the soul, sharpen the sense of right, awaken the energies and quicken the pace of all who fall under these benign influences.

"I am not sure, not very sure, that all the people of Zelania are worthy participators in these noble benefactions; I am only explaining the facts of the situation, the generous sentiment that so largely prevails among the people, and the purposes and intentions of the makers of the law.

"Of course Zelanian statesmen may need to remind the people, that increased effort will be demanded for every opportunity given, and that for personal success, energy, self reliance and hustle must be wholly relied upon, or there may be some misunderstanding."

Whoever leans heavily upon the Government—not the language of the chaste Oseba—usually gets tired easy, so while it is well to furnish every passenger with a life preserver, the fellow who is too lazy to kick deserves to die at sea, to save funeral expenses.

"But, my children," says Mr. Oseba, with rather a human smile, "as it is much less wearisome to put on avoirdupois than to put on grey matter, the social millennium has not yet become firmly seated, even in Zelania."

But, Mr. Oseba, they are steaming up and they will get there all the same, for now that the light has been turned on, the audience will encourage the players to grander performances.

In all changes in life there are sorrows. We come into, and go out of life with pain. In every advance some are left behind, by every improvement some hand is left idle, until it is trained to a new duty. Every economic advance violates some custom under which hoary wrongs found an honored refuge.

But I conclude, from many pages, that Zelania's labor laws are still imperfect, as the leaders themselves recognise, by further improving them. But she is safe in her situation, and these eternal principles of justice are destined to exercise a wide influence throughout the world, for improved light always gives the whole plant a more symmetrical growth.

To the undeviating progress of the industrial situation of Zelania, the world is indebted, first, of course, to her unparalleled natural conditions, second to the intelligence of her people, then to her progressive statesmen, and especially to R. J. Seddon and the able men who have constituted his political family. These, without tradition, history or precedent, have raised the industrial plane of the country to a condition approaching the social ideal— as per mandate.

Like Bolivar and Lincoln and many other of humanity's torch bearers, Mr. Seddon, by the force of his own genius, arose from the industrial walks of life. His was not a meteor flight bursting resplendently upon a startled world; but faithfully biding his time, he came prepared, and evidently he came to stay—for the time of his leave-taking has not yet been announced.

Kiwi. / Milford Sound.

"Mr. Seddon was born a true Briton. He was toughened by colonial experience, his hands were calloused with honest toil, his muscles were hardened with heroic struggles, his intellect was developed by a broad and intelligent observation of interesting events; and he belonged to, arose from, and came forward to serve the people.

"He knew but one rank, that of the free citizen; but one guide, the people's voice; but one master, that of duty—as he understood the command.

"Well, an upper seat became vacant, and, having a ripe experience in parliamentary affairs, appreciative authority, with inviting tones, remarked, 'Richard, come up higher,' and he joined a strong Cabinet. He did his duty as he felt it, and was a part of Zelania's most progressive laws. He ripened with the ever-changing seasons.

"Events hastened; the public appetite was whetted, and said, 'More!' Mr. Ballance, a beloved Premier, foolishly died, a still higher seat was vacant, and again appreciative authority said, 'Richard, come up higher.' He became Premier—the most responsible position in any country ruled under the British parliamentary system—in 1893, and for ten years, with the strength of a Hercules, the courage of an Ajax, and the industry of an Ixion, he has courageously worked in extending, amending, pruning and consolidating the industrial rules of Zelania, until the world that first looked on with amusement, and then with inquiring interest, now beholds with admiration the successful workings of an industrial theory that gives hope to humanity.

"He was a product of the times. The opportunities came, and he harmonised the conditions with the interests and the aspirations of his countrymen, and, without the use of an elevator, he has reached the dome of the temple.

"The labor laws, like the land laws, are based upon the enlightened selfishness of the people in their organised capacity, the idea being, not that everyone may, but that everyone must, earn his or her own living—must be a producer and not a pauper, a tax-payer and not a vagrant. This is democracy.

"The people are not kept, but they are allowed opportunities to keep themselves; they are not aided as a charity, but they are enabled, as a right, to earn and to have, and to contribute to the general well-being of the country.

"In Zelania the soil is a basis of wealth; capital and labor are the active factors, and society, for the good of each and all, proposes that these factors shall peacefully pursue the joint enterprise of production, according to the dictates of justice and humanity.

"It is selfish, of course. Capital must be secure, and industry must necessarily move her tireless wheels. Then society, as a whole, having an interest in each of its members, and a stake in the proceeds, must be the arbiter in all industrial disputes, and the interested parties, being loyal members of the social compact, must yield obedience to the public will."

Well, that is worth embalming!

They numbered the people. If high or low,
Was not worth asking; enough to know
That each had wants; and, that all might live,
Those receiving must willingly give.
Then strove they in love, and not in hate,
To build for aye this matchless State;
For they knew that a temple could not endure
That enriched the baron, and crushed the poor.

"Society," continued the sage, "made up of the industrial cells, requires the security of every shilling, the service of every member, and the peaceful co-operation of all the factors in every industrial enterprise, and as it has not yet been determined how much of our imagined 'natural rights' we may be called upon to yield for the general good, the passionless decision of the public will, for the time being at least, must be the only guide.

"Under the benign *ægis* of a rule, bearing the lengthened legend, 'The Industrial Conciliation and Arbitration Act,' there serenely reposes the most perfect industrial security known in this discontented world. The Labour Laws of Zelania may be 'experimental,' but they sprang from the soul of the public conscience, they were moulded by a desire to secure impartial justice, and for many years they have given a degree of industrial peace, stability, and prosperity, that has won the favour of the general citizenship, and is now exciting the surprise and winning the admiration of the world.

"Then, to cap the climax, my children," said Mr. Oseba, "of all the measures ever calculated to confirm the claims of the Master as to the 'brotherhood' of man, it has been ordained in Zelania that, under liberal provisions, all persons above the full age of sixty-five years, shall be entitled to a life pension."

In harmony with other liberal legislation, support for these measures was asked, Oseba informs his people, not as a matter of charity, but of justice, for it seems to have been held that as members of an industrial community, all worthy persons were supposed to have entitled themselves to a living, and that those who found themselves indigent at that age, had either met with misfortune, or had failed to receive a just equivalent for his or her contribution to the public wealth. There, it seems to be recognised that the world owes, to all men, a living, and that these pensions are advances made to those who have failed to "collect" what was properly due to them. Rather new.[G]

A public sentiment that, above the taint of charity, coins its "respect for worthy old age" into sovereigns, that may be "demanded as a right," by the deserving, stands as far above the pious cant of other countries—as philosophy stands above superstition.

Indolence, poverty, sorrow and want are common to human society, and benevolence and charity have been lauded as saving virtues for many ages; but here, where new ideas seem to generate spontaneously, there has arisen a novel notion—that so closely is the world akin, that the very fact of a person having taken the pains to be born, to behave pretty well, to float to Zelania at the proper time and to exist for sixty-five years, justly entitles him or her to £18 worth of annual "respect."

"This is novel indeed," says Mr. Oseba, "and this notion, in its conceptions of human relationship, social duty and moral responsibility, is nobler than all the sermons—save one—ever preached on this little globe.

"R. J. Seddon is no saint; I am told, my children, he gets angry, he storms, and he may use cuss words, but no poet, priest or philanthropist ever uttered nobler thoughts than he, in his championship of this progressive measure.

Only the dreamer can realise the far-reaching moral grandeur, not of the measure itself, but of the lofty sentiment upon which it is based—and the Premier claimed to speak 'for the people.'

"Considering the general backwardness of the Outeroos in breaking old traditions and especially in the direction of a greater recognition of human brotherhood, or the rights of the individual as a unit of society, the Zelanians have another rule, even more surprising, as you will see, for it is not only the offspring of a sentiment or idea, as novel in its nobility of conception as that upon which grew the old age pension, but it is so radical a departure from old British customs, as to startle a student with its audacious demands.

"In the older lands the desire, as well as the custom, is to erect commanding fortunes and to perpetuate wealthy and powerful families—though many of the kindred struggle through miserable lives in poverty; but in Zelania, should a person who contemplates permanent 'retirement,' endeavor by will or 'last testament,' to leave all his belongings to the 'white headed boy,' or otherwise fail to provide, according to his means, for the 'proper maintenance and support' of any of his dependents, the Courts 'may go back of the returns,' inquire into the matter, practically annul 'said will,' and make such provisions as 'shall seem fit,' according to the demands of open-handed justice.

"Zelania recognises every person as an integral part of the social group, with reciprocal rights and duties. An individual may pray with and prey upon the community and acquire 'much riches,' and, as the legal custodian of this 'lucre,' he has considerable latitude; but, as a fact, he is only a trustee, and when he leaves his money in this world—lest it should melt—he is not allowed to deprive any of his dependents who may remain for a time as members of the community, of all 'consolation' for his departure.[H]

"Contrary to the general notions of outside barbarians, the advanced legislation in Zelania is not the result of an erratic temperament, but of advanced thought, of a nobler conception of human duty, and a higher ideal of social progress.

"Zelania as a social entity is not a commanding empire. She points to no glorious traditions, to no rivers of blood, to no ancient splendors with ruined aqueducts, fallen columns or ivy-grown temples; no chained captives and moss-grown universities, where hoots the hooded owl; but representing a new phase of intellectual aspiration, her sturdy statesmen have planted the banner of social progress beyond the dreams of other lands, and they have made her the most interesting, the most hopeful, and, socially, the most conspicuous spot on the broad surface of Oliffa."

Eloquent in his recital, Mr. Oseba closed this topic:—

"The time is hurriedly coming, my children, when the statues of Zelanian statesmen who have pushed to their full realisation the noble principles, towards which humanity has been vainly struggling for countless ages, will adorn the most popular niches, galleries, and squares of the world's most civilised centres."

SOME PLEASANT OUTINGS.

Here Mr. Oseba runs off on a pleasing tangent, and he leads us to the conclusion that a tour of Zelania is a jaunt of unrivalled pleasure; so full of change, of variety and surprising incidents, that curiosity lashes one forward, and physical vigor so rapidly improves as to banish all thought of weariness. On these tours good health is actually "catching," and the appetite always arrives before meal time.

He describes in interesting detail the ease, safety and comfort, as well as the jocund hilarity, of these kaleidoscopic gyrations, and how easily, with a word and a wire from Mr. T. E. Donne, the candid and competent tourist manager, one may find the path to the noblest scenes.

"That time may not hang heavily on the spring bathers, millions of fish—better than Peter ever hauled from the Sea of Galilee—are waiting in many lakes for the tempting fly, and if one tires of glacier climbing in the South, the woods are full of red deer, and other nimble game, waiting to give him a wilder sport.

A Stag's Head

"As for climate, I conclude that one may choose that as he chooses his drinks, for he may have sunshine or shower, chilling glacier or burning valley, frozen or boiling lakes, simply by switching on or off a new path. The weather is 'almost always' good, and as one may dodge a storm by going fishing, instead of going mountain climbing, or a hot wave by stalking deer instead of hunting geysers or Maori maidens, bad weather is not worth talking about."

Then he turns the globe and shows that Zelania is in the Southern Hemisphere, and he expects that as soon as his discoveries are made known, many thousands of people—to avoid the severe cold winters of Europe and America—will spend a season of eternal spring among those romantic scenes. Here Mr. Oseba grows eloquent. I quote:—

"As bare-handed Nature, by her almost infinite allurements, spanked the rude savage of Zelania into an eloquent politician, so she improves upon every animal turned loose upon her palpitating bosom. Bring a little starved rabbit to Zelania—well, it does not become a tiger the same afternoon, but it soon begins business, and in a brief period it has the 'lord of creation' on the defensive—for it is eating him out.

"The offspring of every animal, every bird, every lake, brook or river fish, brought to Zelania, in a very short time greatly improves in size and beauty. Well, so it is with people."

ENCORE ZELANIA.

Again thy face, Sapho, though thou hast won the crown,
The moon hangs high, return, let's laugh till she goes down.

The notes of Leo Bergin record no sign of weariness, either on the part of the audience or the orator. The sittings had been prolonged, but a cheerful and most intelligent interest seemed to have been preserved throughout, and the closing scenes in the review of Zelania had almost aroused enthusiasm. The curtain had been rolled down for a brief intermission, and as it was known that the last act was now to be staged, all the anxiety and freshness of a new sitting were manifest in the audience.

The lantern appliances had been removed, and it was evident that the conclusions of these unique proceedings were very near. The notes say:—

"Oseba arose, and when he stepped to the footlights, and indicated his readiness to proceed, he was greeted with an applause well becoming a Boston audience on the appearance of a Webster."

Here the poetess Vauline, apologising for the interruption at so late a stage in the proceedings, ventured to inquire by what course of reasoning the sage Oseba had reached his conclusions that the Anglo-Saxon was destined to a universal supremacy, and why the Zelanians should now be regarded as the torch-bearers of the future ages?

With a smile of approval Mr. Oseba answered:—

"The question is timely and important. Following the laws of natural progress up to a certain point, survival depends largely on the thickness of the skin and the length of the claws, but, above that point, it is a question of grey matter, and the Anglo-Saxon has brains in his head. Well, the Zelanians are a picked squad on the skirmish line of the Anglo-Saxon legions."

Here again I "boil down," and note my own conclusions from Mr. Oseba's argument:—

The Anglo-Saxon intellect is the product of more than 1,400 years of unparalleled vicissitudes, and by its inherent virtue it has resistless force. Progress is a question of intellectual development, of susceptibility, adaptability, and adjustability of a people, and in the constitution of this racial brain are found all these traits in full measure. Besides, in the Anglo-Saxon character there are found a solid sincerity and love of justice, that inspire a respect and confidence that are irresistible. It is a matter of brain—of ideal.

The ideals of Assyria, Persia, and Babylonia were Empire—military conquest, and we see passing over the stage but kingly splendor, and, as a background, the gods that lashed the people—if there were any—into loyal obedience.

The ideal of Egypt was durability—to eternise the works of kings—based upon a religious idea, and she erected the Pyramids, still the wonder of the world's wonders.

The ideal of Phœnicia was commerce, and the ship was the type of her realised dream. Here the city was greater than the empire, and the merchant was greater than the king.

The ideal of Greece was beauty—then personal beauty—in form and character. Under the reign of this ideal came her noblest achievements. But the Greek brain was erratic; the Greek heroes were soon deified. The artist came, and when the marble statue became the ideal and also the idol, the Greek philosopher became a sophist, and Greece fell a prey to a more practical race.

The ideal of Rome was power, force and the glamour of Patrician splendor. That the lower orders might fight more bravely for the further aggrandisement of the holy city, they were fed on barley buns and flattered with an imaginary freedom, but the ideal of Rome was force.

The ideals of Venice and Genoa were wealth, luxury and art, and their palaces and cathedrals—still the wonder and admiration of the world—became their realised dreams; but only these, and the folly of the Doge, remain to us.

The ideal of Spain—in her greatness—was royal splendor, propped by the spiritual authority, with subject colonies to furnish places for favorites and revenues for the State.

The ideals of Britain were trade, the factory, the shop, the ship, and the "old family"—to occupy the easy seats. But these British ideals developed individual enterprise, and soon it was discovered that in Britain there were people. Save for a few brief periods in Attica, from the fall of Israel to the rise of Britain the *people* cut little figure in recorded history.

The ideal of America, say up to the passing of Lincoln, was personal liberty, and under this sentiment she produced some of the noblest characters that ever stood erect and wore the image of God. But the gates were turned in, millions came from afar, the earlier sentiments were perverted, great wealth became the master motive, and dollars have become the national ideal.

All these countries have succeeded, if Mr. Oseba's arguments are valid, in some measure in developing the "master motive," or in realising the national ideal.

"Well, my children," said Oseba, "the force of Zelania as a social leader is also in her ideals, and as the conspicuous happiness and prosperity of a people are the best evidence of a benign rule, the appreciation of her ideals has proved their utilitarian virtues.

"Well, by some exploit in mental gymnastics, the Zelanians have chosen the highest possible ideal, Justice—the enthronement of the individual—and with the inherited instincts of the race and a most favorable environment, it was to be expected that, with the ripening of the yearnings of man, humanity should find its highest type in these Romantic Isles.

"In closing, allow me briefly to recall to your minds a few of the more important features of my argument on these most interesting themes.

"I have reminded you, my children, that liberty never gained a victory in an old, well-established, and wealthy nation.

"I have reminded you that with great wealth and population people become conservative, the rulers cling to inherited power, the wealthy fear change, and the mass, by custom becoming loyal, reform is impossible—or at best, progress is slow indeed.

"I have reminded you that commerce is the basis of modern civilisation, but that only people inhabiting the water-front have ever become sufficiently commercial to materially influence any considerable portion of mankind; and I have reminded you that it was only through the colonial enterprise of commercial nations that the great progressive movements have been carried on.

"Further, I have reminded you that only in the colonies, in new and isolated communities, far removed from central authority, where novel conditions required novel methods, is self-reliance nourished, liberty aroused, and social progress made possible.

"And, I have also further reminded you, that of all the tribes, races, or nations that ever loafed about the earth's surface, those of Phœnicia, Greece, and Britain were alone capable of breaking away from inherited customs, and asserting freedom of action, or of so adjusting themselves to the requirements of a new environment as to develop a state of society differing materially from that of the old order of things.

"Then, too, I have shown you the social outposts of all the nations, and how improbable it is that they should advance any further by their own inherent force.

"I have reminded you also, that the total or aggregate of human rights is the same in all states, regardless of form or population, that, like elbow-room, individual rights decrease as the numbers participating increase, and that of all things a great population is least to be desired, and an over-population the most to be dreaded.

"But Zelania occupies a unique position. She has no traditions, she has no overlord, no organised trusts, no vested rights in hoary wrongs; she has no withering precedents, no millionaire monopolies howling for victims, and having room for many millions she may bide her time, and if she cares for more people she may make her own selection.

"With her numberless wonders to attract the tourist, her splendid opportunities for profitable industry, and her more wonderful social situation to attract the inquiring thousands from many lands, she will soon become, with sagacious management, the Mecca of the world's leisured wealthy, and from these will come the best of all 'invaders.'

"My children, with all these splendid facts, I would not advise the empty-handed to rush to Zelania, hoping to secure an easy livelihood; but no person with an inquiring mind who loves Nature, who feels an interest in the social progress of his race, and who is possessed of moderate means, should allow himself to quit this fair and interesting life, without visiting this most charming of all lands, this paragon of social happiness, this paradise of Oliffa.

"Many of you, my children, after having read my report, and having meditated more deeply upon the pleasures and profits of travel and observation, will make this pleasing visit, and should the hospitable people of Zelania meet any quiet, dignified, well-regulated stranger, who says little, but sees and hears everything, who inquires without criticising, admires without flattery, lends freely to all his friends, and pays his own bills, they may 'guess' that he is a 'gentleman' from 'Symmes' Hole.'

"Measures, my children, the character of which would shock the tender sensibilities of those who assume to be the saviours of society, have vindicated the wisdom of Zelania's statesmen—by the demonstrated applicability of these measures to the necessities of modern progress.

"Of all spots on the surface of Oliffa, this Zelania is most charming, and of all people on the surface of Oliffa, these Zelanians have made the greatest social advance, and occupy the most favored position for future usefulness.

"Then, with all these masterful advantages, with an ideal country, capable of supporting many millions of people, she holds—with a small number of the choicest of the race—her own destinies in her own hands.

"So, my children, there is hope for the world. Genius has annihilated time and space, commerce has brought humanity so in touch, that the light of inspiration may come from without, and seeing the beacon from afar, the oppressed of many nations will arouse and demand 'a little more light.'"

Great idea, Mr. Oseba, worthy of the "Poet's Lore," for though the watchman on the tower may be slow in gaining a glimpse, his keen eye will finally behold its glowing effulgence.

With faith he hath struggled for reason and right,
Withdrew from the darkness in search of the light;
With face to the morning, and gazing afar,
O'er Southern horizons he spies a new star,
And cries, "Hail, Zelania! though distant thou be,
Welcome thy light shining over the sea;
Welcome thy flag, to the heavens unfurled,
The beacon, the guide, and the hope of the world."

Stage Road, Buller Gorge.

"Zelania is like unto another prophet, teaching from the mountain top. The blaze of her divine torch is not of a fitful glare, but the genial rays of its steady glow are so spreading over all the earth, that the people of all lands may soon behold and wonder, and inquire, and then emulate.

"Well, my children, the tales of my strange adventures are well-nigh told. The curtain will soon fall, and while the lessons from these happy sittings will remain with us as but fading memories, the wonders of this enchanting land will thrill and fill the inquiring souls of men for all time—for the day of Zelania is just at the dawn.

"Inspired by an inherited instinct, and guided by Anglo-Saxon genius, civilisation has won more victories since the crowning of Victoria than during all the generations from 'Saul of Tarsus' to Paul of Pretoria, and

Zelania is away in the vanguard of the great progressive social force that is destined to enlighten the brain and unfetter the limbs of humanity.

"It is manifest destiny that Anglo-Saxon aspiration, language, and civilisation should dominate the world. With the realisation of this hope, business interests will prevent war; despotism will be good-naturedly hissed from the stage; Europe will be commercially united; production and exchange will be so adjusted as to employ all willing hands; the arsenals will become factories; the great guns will be stood erect as pillars in historic museums; the muskets will be cast into gas pipes, and swords into sheep-shears, and the gods will look down and smile upon the first generation of truly civilised men!

"Then, at the consummation of these noble purposes, when a monument shall have been erected in honor of those who led in the emancipation of humanity, on the highest tablet on the Temple of Eternal Fame, and in letters of imperishable splendor, shall be emblazoned,—

'ZELANIA.'"

FOOTNOTES

[A] The Remarkable Mountains, on the easterly side of Lake Wakatipu, S. Island.

[B] Lands for Settlement Act.

[C] During the 19th century the common use of the English language increased over 500 per cent., as against 150 per cent. for the German, 102 for the Italian, and about 66 for the French and Spanish. It is practically the business, and is rapidly becoming the "polite" language of the "civilised" world.

[D] The Industrial Conciliation and Arbitration Act, 1900, with amendments.

[E] Employers Liability Act, 1882, practically superseded by The Workers Compensation for Accident, 1900, Act.

[F] Government Accident Insurance Act, 1899.

[G] Old Age Pension Act, 1898.

[H] Testators' Family Maintenance Act.

Milton Keynes UK
Ingram Content Group UK Ltd.
UKHW011123180424
441376UK00004B/173